PRIMARY MATHEMATICS 4A Home Instructor's Guide

Authored by: Jennifer Hoerst
Printed by: Avyx, Inc.

Published by Avyx, Inc.
Reprinted 2005, 2007, 2010

Go to:
www.avyx.com

Or e-mail:
info@avyx.dom

Or write:
Avyx, Inc.
8032 South Grant Way
Littleton, CO 80122-2705
USA
303-483-0140

ISBN 13: 978-1-887-84093-4

Printed in the United States of America

Preface and General Instructions

This guide is meant to help instructors using *Primary Mathematics 3B* when teaching one student or a small group of students. It should be used as a guide and adapted as needed. It contains

 objectives,

 notes to the instructor, providing added explanation of concepts,

 instructional ideas and suggested activities,

 and ideas for games

to reinforce concepts from the

 corresponding textbook pages, learning tasks, and

 "homework" assignments.

Included is a <u>suggested</u> weekly schedule and pages for mental math (in the appendix). The schedule is simply to help you keep on track – you need to spend more time on a topic if necessary and less time if your student is proficient in the topic. Practices and reviews in the text are scheduled as they are encountered, and can be done independently by the student, or can be used as part of a lesson. Since some of the practice questions are challenging, they provide good opportunities for discussion. When there are several practices one after the other, you may want to go on to the next topic and insert the rest of the practices later to allow for more ongoing review. The mental math pages can be used as worksheets and many can also be done orally, with your student seeing the problem and answering out loud rather than writing the answer down. They can be used any time after they are referenced in this guide, and can be used more than once for more practice. So if four Mental Math pages are listed for one lesson, they are not meant to all be done during that lesson, but can be used any time after that lesson for review and mental math practice.

Answers to the workbook exercises are given at the end of this guide.

This guide can be used with both the third edition and the U.S. edition of *Primary Mathematics 4A*.

3d› indicates portions pertaining only to the third edition, and

US› indicates portions pertaining only to the US edition (except for number words).

U.S. spellings and conventions will be used in this guide. Answers involving number words will use the current U.S. convention of reserving the word "and" for the decimal and not using it in number words for whole numbers.

Contents

Answers to Workbook Exercises and Reviews

Weekly Schedule

	Part	Lesson	Text Pages	Workbook Exercises	Mental Math (appendix)	Additional Material
Unit 1 : Whole Numbers						
1	1 Numbers to 100,000	(1) Ten Thousand	6-8	1	1, 2	Number discs Place value cards Playing cards or number cards
		(2) Place Value	9-10	2-3		
		(3) Add, Subtract, Multiply, and Divide Thousands	11	4		
	2 Rounding Off Numbers	(1) Rounding to the Nearest 10	12-14	5	3, 4	Hundred chart Number lines (in appendix)
2		(2) Rounding to the Nearest 100	15-16	6		
		(3) Estimation	17	7		
		(4) Practice	18			
	3 Factors	(1) Factors (2) Common Factors	19-20 20-21	8 9	5, 6	Linking cubes Hundred chart Factor Game Board
3	4 Multiples	(1) Multiples	23-26	10		
		(2) Practice	27			
Unit 2 : Multiplication and Division of Whole Numbers						
	1 Multiplication by a 1-Digit Number, Division by a 1-Digit Number and by 10	(1) Multiplication by a 1-Digit Number	28, 30	11		Place-value cards, base-10 blocks, or number discs
		(2) Division by a 1-Digit Number	29, 31-33	12, #1		
4		(3) Division by 10	31-32	12. #2	7	
		(4) Word Problems	33-34	13		
		(5) Practice	35			
	2 Multiplication by a 2-Digit Number	(1) Multiplication by Tens	36-38	14	8	Base-10 blocks or number discs
5		(2) Multiplication by a 2-Digit Number	38-39	15 16		
		(3) Practice	40			
Review						
	Review			Review 1	9-12	
Unit 3 : Fractions						
6	1 Adding Fractions	(1) Equivalent Fractions				Fraction bars Fraction circles
		(2) Adding Like Fractions	42-43	17		
		(3) Adding Related Fractions	44-45	18		
	2 Subtracting Fractions	(1) Subtracting Like Fractions	46-47	19		
7		(2) Subtracting Related Fractions	48-49	20		
		(3) Word Problems with Fractions		21		
		(4) Practice	50		13-14	
		(5) Practice	51			

	Part	Lesson	Text Pages	Workbook Exercises	Mental Math (appendix)	Additional Material
8	3 Mixed Numbers	(1) Mixed Numbers	52-53	22	15	Ruler
	4 Improper Fractions	(1) Improper Fractions	54-55	23		
		(2) Converting Improper Fractions to Mixed Numbers	56	24		Fraction circles Fraction bars
		(3) Converting Mixed Numbers to Improper Fractions	56-57	25		
9		(4) Adding and Subtracting Fractions	57	26	16	
				Review 2		
10	5 Fraction of a Set	(1) The Fraction of a Set	58-59	27		Two-color counters or coins
		(2) Amount in a Fraction of a Set	59	28		
		(3) Multiplication of a Fraction and a Whole Number I	60	29		
		(4) Multiplication of a Fraction and a Whole Number II	60	30	17-18	
11		(5) Word Problems I	61	31		Coins, dollar bill
		(6) Fraction of a Whole	61-62	32		
		(7) Word Problems II	62	33		
		(8) Two Step Word Problems	63-64	34 35		
12		(9) Practice	65			
	Review			Review 3		
Unit 4 : Tables and Graphs						
13	1 Presenting Data	(1) Tables and Bar Graphs	70-71	36 37		Graph paper
		(2) Bar Graphs	72	38		
		(3) Tables	73	39		
		(4) Collecting and Presenting Data		40		
Unit 5 : Angles						
14	1 Measuring Angles	(1) Measuring Angles	74-75	41		Protractor
		(2) Constructing Angles	75	42		
		(3) Angles Greater than 180°	76-77	43		
		(4) Finding Unknown Angles	77	44		

	Part	Lesson	Text Pages	Workbook Exercises	Mental Math (appendix)	Additional Material
Unit 6 : Perpendicular and Parallel Lines						
15	1 Perpendicular Lines	(1) Identifying Perpendicular Lines	78-79	45		Set-square (triangle) Square grid paper Ruler
		(2) Constructing Perpendicular Lines	80	46		
	2 Parallel Lines	(1) Identifying Parallel Lines	81-82	47		
		(2) Constructing Parallel Lines	83	48		
Unit 7 : Area and Perimeter and Review						
16	1 Rectangles and Squares	(1) Area and Perimeter	84-86	49		Centimeter graph paper Rectangle cut-outs
	2 Composite Figures	(1) Perimeter of Composite Figures	87-88	50		
		(2) Area of Composite Figures	89	51		
		(3) Area of Paths	90	52		
17		(4) Practice	91-93			
	Review			Review 4		

Additional Material

Base-10 set.

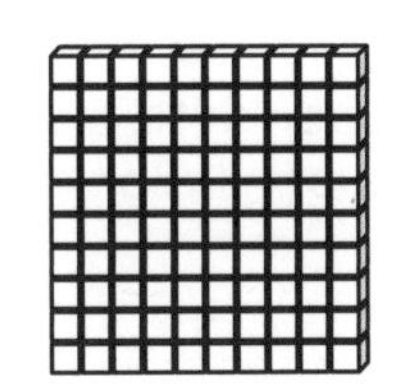

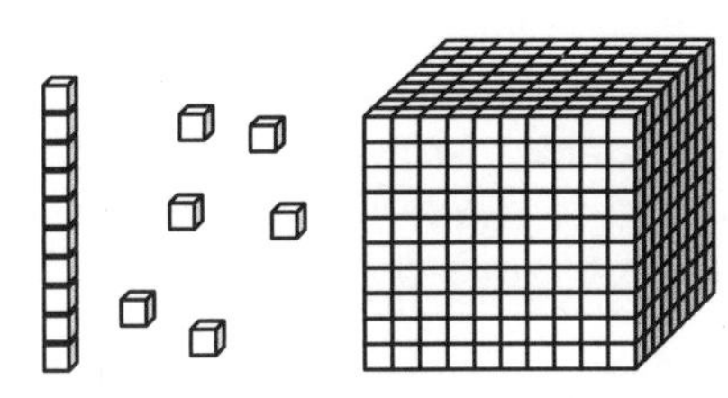

Number discs
Use plastic or cardboard discs and write "100,000" on one disc, "10,000" on twenty discs, "1000" on twenty discs, "100" on twenty discs, "10" on twenty discs, and "1" on twenty discs.

Multilink cubes
Cubes that link together, preferably on all sides.

Place-Value Chart
The chat should be large enough to hold up to nine number discs each in the top and bottom halves. A ten-thousand column is optional.

Ten thousands	Thousands	Hundreds	Tens	Ones

Place-Value Cards
You can copy the cards in the appendix onto tag board (manila folders cut to page size) and cut out. Cut the corners off. Make 4-5 of each card if using them for games.

Hundred-Chart
Make one or buy one with squares large enough to hold counters or coins.

1	2	3	4	5	6	7	8	9	10
11	12	13	14	15	16	17	18	19	20
21	22	23	24	25	26	27	28	29	30
31	32	33	34	35	36	37	38	39	40
41	42	43	44	45	46	47	48	49	50
51	52	53	54	55	56	57	58	59	60
61	62	63	64	65	66	67	68	69	70
71	72	73	74	75	76	77	78	79	80
81	82	83	84	85	86	87	88	89	90
91	92	93	94	95	96	97	98	99	100

Transparent counters
These should cover up the numbers on a hundred chart (or just use a small object that doesn't cover up the number completely.

Two-color counters (or use coins).

Index cards for number cards and fact cards.

Playing cards or **4 sets of number cards 0-10**
Use two decks. For one deck, remove the face cards and white out the 1 and the symbols on the tens card to make it into a 0. Aces are ones. For the other deck, remove the face cards but leave the tens.

Dice

12-inch ruler
Use a ruler that shows inches on one side and centimeters on the other. Use one that shows 16ths from 0 to 6 inches and tenths from 6 to 12 inches.

Fraction circles and **fraction bars**.
There are some in the appendix that can be copied onto tag-board and cut out. Commercial circles and bars are more durable.

Protractor

Set-square
These are triangles with either 90°-45°-45° angles or 90°-60°-30° angles. Plastic ones can usually be bought in a set with a ruler, protractor, and sometimes a compass in the school supply section of most department stores.

Unit 1 Whole Numbers

Part 1 Numbers to 100,000

(1) Ten-Thousands (pp. 6-8)

- Read and write 5-digit numbers.

In *Primary Mathematics 3A*, students learned to relate 4-digit numbers to the place value concept and to order numbers within 10,000. This is extended here to 5-digit numbers.

Page 6

Ask:	Write
	1
How many one dollar bills do we change for ten dollars? (10) There are ten times as many dollars in a ten dollar bill than in a one dollar bill. We show this by writing a 1 in the tens column, and a 0 in the ones column as a place holder. The number that goes in each place is called a **digit**. What digit is in the tens place? (1) What digit is in the ones place? (0)	1 0
How many ten dollar bills do we change for one hundred dollars? (10) To show 10 tens, we need another place, the hundreds place. Each place is ten times more than the place to the right.	1 0 0
How many hundred dollars do we change for one thousand dollars? (10) We need to make another place to show 10 hundreds. Sometimes we write a comma after the thousands place.	1, 0 0 0
How many thousand dollars do we change for ten thousand dollars? (10) We need to make another place to show 10 thousands. This is called the ten-thousand place. We always write a comma after the thousands place when we have more than 4 places, or digits, in the number.	1 0, 0 0 0

Page 7

Have your student read the numbers and number words. Remind her that we put a dash between tens and ones for numbers greater than 20, and point out that we put a comma after the word "thousand."

Use **number discs**. Mix them up in a bag. Have your student draw out a predetermined number of discs, such as 25, and arrange them on a **place-value chart** and then writes the number and the number word.

Or, use **place-value cards**. Shuffle in separate stacks of ten thousands, thousands, hundreds, tens, and ones. The student draws one card from each stack and writes the resulting number and number word.

Or, write or say some numbers or number words and have your student write the corresponding number words or numbers.

Page 8
Learning Tasks 1-2, p. 8

1. (a) two thousand, seven hundred fifty-three
   (b) seven thousand, nine hundred nineteen
   (c) four thousand, nine hundred eight
   (d) three thousand, fifty-six
   (e) seven thousand, two hundred eighty
   (f) five thousand, two
   (g) twenty seven thousand, one hundred sixty-five
   (h) eighteen thousand, fifty-seven
   (i) forty-two thousand, six hundred five
   (j) thirty thousand, three
   (k) sixty thousand, one hundred nine
   (l) eighty-one thousand, nine hundred

2. (a) 8012 (b) 49,501
   (c) 17,004 (d) 90,090

Workbook Exercise 1

(2) Place Value (pp. 9-10)

- Relate each digit in a 5-digit number to its place value.
- Add or subtract 1, 10, 100, 1000, or 10,000 for a given number less than 100,000.
- Order numbers within 100,000.

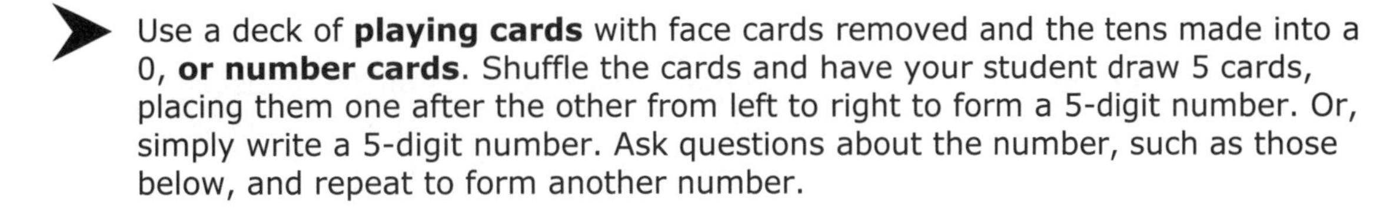

➤ Use a deck of **playing cards** with face cards removed and the tens made into a 0, **or number cards**. Shuffle the cards and have your student draw 5 cards, placing them one after the other from left to right to form a 5-digit number. Or, simply write a 5-digit number. Ask questions about the number, such as those below, and repeat to form another number.

Ask for the digit in a certain place, such as:

Which digit is in the thousands place?
What is the value of the digit ...?

Then, ask her to write the number that is 1, 10, 100, 1000, or 10,000 more or less than the given number. Be sure to include numbers where regrouping becomes necessary. For example:

What number is 1000 more than 19,946? (20,946)
What number is 100 less than 13,040? (12,940)

You may want to extend this to numbers that are 2, 20, 200, 2000, or 20,000 more or less than the given number, or 3, 30, 300, 3000, or 30,000 more or less than the given number.

➤ Give your student some number patterns and ask her to extend the pattern. One of the digits should increase or decrease by 1 or 2.

12,345; 12,445; 12,545; ...
13,010; 12,010; 11,010; ...
37,004; 47,004; 57,004; ...

You may want to do some patterns where one number increases and another decreases.

46,934; 47,924; 48,914; ...
7531; 8530; 9529; ...

➤ Write down some numbers, one above the other, with similar digits. Have your student compare the numbers by first looking at each place value in turn, starting with the largest. For example: 46,832 and 46,823. First we compare the digits in the ten-thousands place. They are the same, so then we compare the digits in the thousands place. They are the same, so then we compare the digits in the hundreds place. They are the same, so then we compare the digits in the tens place. 46,832 is smaller than 46,823 since it has a smaller number in the tens place. Compare a few other numbers, such as

32,109; 31,209; 32,901 83,002; 83,200; 82,300

Learning Tasks 3-9, pp. 9-11

3.

5000	6000	7000	8000	9000	10,000	11,000
29,500	29,600	29,700	29,800	29,900	30,000	30,100
			28,800		40,000	
24,230			27,800		50,000	
24,120			26,800		60,000	
24,030			25,800		70,000	
23,930			24,800			
23,830	23,820	23,810	23,800	23,790	23,780	23,770
23,730						
23,630	23,640	23,650	23,660	23,670	23,680	23,690

4. 8000; 60,000

5. (a) 800 (b) 80,000 (c) 8000

6. (b) 35,260 (c) 2 (d) 3
   (e) 3: 30,000 5: 5000
   2: 200 6: 60 0: 0

7. (b) 345 (c) 20,000

8. Discuss how to find the value of each division. We can divide the number of divisions between two numbers on the number line by the difference between those numbers. In (a), there are 5 units between 5000 and 5500, a difference of 500, so each division is 100. In (b), there are 5 units between 50,000 and 55,000, a difference of 5,000, so each division is 1,000
   (a) A: 5100 B: 5300 C: 5700
   D: 5900 E: 6400
   (b) P: 49,000 Q: 52,000 R: 54,000
   S: 58,000 T: 61,000

9. (a) 56,700 (b) 32,645

Highest number

Material: Playing cards with face cards removed and 10's marked as 0's, or 4 sets of number cards 0-9.

Procedure: Shuffle cards and place face down between the players. Each player takes turns drawing 5 cards and forms a 5-digit number. The player with the highest number wins the round. The one to win the most rounds or to win a specified number of rounds first, wins. Reshuffle the cards if all are drawn before the game ends.

Workbook Exercises 2 and 3

(3) Add, Subtract, Multiply, and Divide Thousands (p. 11)

- Add and subtract thousands and ten thousands.
- Multiply and divide thousands and ten thousands.

In earlier levels of *Primary Mathematics* students learned a variety of techniques for mentally adding 2-digit numbers. In *Primary Mathematics 3A*, they learned to add and subtract 4-digit numbers, and to multiply and divide tens and hundreds by 1-digit numbers. These concepts are extended to thousands and ten thousands here. The problems in this section can be done mentally by paying attention to the place values. Multiplication and division of 4-digit numbers by a 1-digit number using the multiplication or division algorithm will be taught in Unit 2 of *Primary Mathematics 4A*.

➤ Discuss the following, using number discs to illustrate if necessary. Mental math techniques for adding and subtracting 2-digit numbers were taught in earlier levels. Your student should be able to do these problems mentally, that is, without rewriting them vertically, by noting the place value.

26 + **9** = **35** — 26 ones + 9 ones = 35 ones
260 + **9**0 = **35**0 — 26 tens + 9 tens = 35 tens
2600 + **9**00 = **35**00 — 26 hundreds + 9 hundreds = 35 hundreds
26,000 + **9**000 = **35**,000 — 26 thousands + 9 thousands = 35 thousands

26 – **9** = **17** — 26 ones – 9 = 17 ones
260 – **9**0 = **17**0 — 26 tens – 9 tens = 17 tens
2600 – **9**00 = **17**00 — 26 hundreds – 9 hundreds = 17 hundreds
26,000 – **9**000 = **17**000 — 26 thousands – 9 thousands = 17 thousands

➤ Discuss the following, using number discs to illustrate if necessary:

2 x **3** = **6** — 2 ones x 3 = 6 ones
20 x **3** = **6**0 — 2 tens x 3 = 6 tens
200 x **3** = **6**00 — 2 hundreds x 3 = 6 hundreds
2000 x **3** = **6**000 — 2 thousands x 3 = 6 thousands
20,000 x **3** = **6**0,000 — 2 ten-thousands x 3 = 6 ten-thousands

5 x **4** = **20** — 5 x 4 ones = 20 ones = 2 tens
5 x **4**0 = **20**0 — 5 x 4 tens = 20 tens = 2 hundreds
5 x **4**00 = **20**00 — 5 x 4 hundreds = 20 hundreds = 2 thousands
5 x **4**000 = **20**,000 — 5 x 4 thousands = 20 thousands = 2 ten-thousands

Show your student that he can cover up the trailing 0's, find the product, and then add back on the trailing 0's. Note that in the second set there are more 0's in the product than in one of the factors – one of the 0's came from the product of 5 and 4.

 Discuss the following, using number discs to illustrate if necessary:

48 ÷ 8 = 6	48 ones ÷ 8 = 6 ones
480 ÷ **8** = **6**0	48 tens ÷ 8 = 6 tens
4800 ÷ **8** = **6**00	48 hundreds ÷ 8 = 6 hundreds
48,000 ÷ **8** = **6**000	48 thousands ÷ 8 = 6 thousands
30 ÷ 6 = 5	30 ones ÷ 6 = 5
300 ÷ **6** = **5**0	30 tens ÷ 6 = 5 tens
3000 ÷ **6** = **5**00	30 hundreds ÷ 6 = 5 hundreds
30,000 ÷ **6** = **5**,000	30 thousands ÷ 6 = 5 thousands

Show your student that he can cover up the 0's in the first number until he gets to a number he recognizes as one that can be divided by the second number, if there is one. For the second set, that number includes a 0 (30). Point out that if he does not get to a number that can be divided by the second number, he will have to do the regular division algorithm, as with 34000 ÷ 5 = 6800.

Additional problems can be found in Mental Math 3-6 in the appendix.
You may want to spend some time reviewing multiplication and division facts with your student.

Learning Task 10, p. 11

10. (a) 14,000 (b) 31,000
(c) 9000 (d) 26,000
(e) 28,000 (f) 50,000
(g) 4000 (h) 5000

Workbook Exercise 4

Part 2 Rounding Off Numbers

(1) Rounding to the Nearest 10 (pp. 12-14)

- Round off whole numbers to the nearest 10.
- Determine the scale of a number line.

Rounding off numbers will be used in estimation.

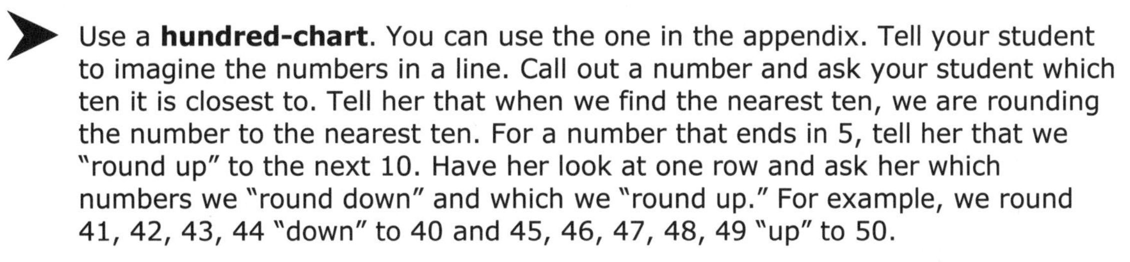

Use a **hundred-chart**. You can use the one in the appendix. Tell your student to imagine the numbers in a line. Call out a number and ask your student which ten it is closest to. Tell her that when we find the nearest ten, we are rounding the number to the nearest ten. For a number that ends in 5, tell her that we "round up" to the next 10. Have her look at one row and ask her which numbers we "round down" and which we "round up." For example, we round 41, 42, 43, 44 "down" to 40 and 45, 46, 47, 48, 49 "up" to 50.

Ask her what 2 is when rounded to the nearest 10. It is 0. 0 can be considered a 10; it is ten less than 10, just as 10 is ten less than 20.

Use the number lines in the appendix, p. a24. For each one, the student must determine the size of the division, or scale. Give her some numbers to mark on them, and have her tell what the number is when rounded to the nearest 10. In the second number line the scale is 2. Give your student an odd number - she should see that it must lie half way between two marks. In the third number line, the scale is 5, so she must estimate how close to a 5 the number must go. In the fourth number line, the scale is 10, so she must already estimate which ten the number is closest to in order to mark it between two lines. For example, if you give her the number 613, she must mark it closer to the mark for 610 than 620.

Ask your student the following: If a number rounded to the nearest 10 is 30, what numbers could it be? It must be 25, 26, 27, 28, 29, 30, 31, 32, 33, or 34. It could be any number between 25 and 34, inclusive.

Page 12-14
Learning Tasks 1-3, p. 14

1.	(a) 30	(b) 40	(c) 80	(d) 100
2.	(a) 230	(b) 1460	(c) 2740	
3.	(a) 130	(b) 200	(c) 450	(d) 690
	(e) 2070	(f) 4360	(g) 4810	(h) 5510

Workbook Exercise 5

(2) Rounding to the Nearest 100 (pp. 15-16)

- Round off whole numbers to the nearest 100.

Use the number lines in the appendix, p. a25. On the first one, have your student note that the scale is 10. Have him locate a number such as 344. He must estimate where to place it; not quite halfway after the fourth mark after 300. Ask him which 10 it is closest to. Then ask him which 100 it is closest to. Do a few others. Give him a number ending in 50, such as 450. Tell him that when a number ends in 50, we "round up" to the next 100. Ask him what we would round 451 to. How about 449?

Ask: If a number rounded to the nearest 100 is 600, what could the number be? It could be any number between 550 and 649, inclusive.

Ask: What is 32 to the nearest 100? (0)

Give him numbers to locate on the other number lines, and have him round them to the nearest 100.

Learning Tasks 4-7, pp. 15-16

4. (a) 2480 (b) 2500
5. 34,100
6. (a) 300 (b) 3700 (c) 4900 (d) 27,100 (e) 42,600
7. (a) 300 (b) 500 (c) 700 (d) 1000
   (e) 2900 (f) 3100 (g) 4300 (h) 5200
   (i) 14,200 (j) 25,500 (k) 32,500 (l) 52,100

Riddles: What number am I?

- I am the largest number that becomes 40 when rounded to the nearest 10 (44)
- I am the smallest number that can become 500 when it is rounded to the nearest 10 (495).
- I am the smallest whole number that can become 500 when it is rounded to the nearest 100. (450)
- I am the largest whole number that can become 500 when it is rounded to the nearest 100. (549)
- I am a number. I am the product of the number of days in a month rounded to the nearest 10 and the number of days in a week rounded to the nearest 10. (300)

Workbook Exercise 6

(3) Estimation (p. 17)

- Estimate the answers in addition and subtraction.

- Tell your student that sometimes it is useful to be able to get an approximate answer to a math problem. For example, when we go shopping, sometimes we want to know about how much several items will cost altogether. Say we have $10 and want to buy two things, one which costs $4.85 and another which costs $3.39, how can we find out if we have enough money? We don't need to find an exact cost of the two items but just need an approximate cost. We can round the first item to $5 and the second to $3. They will cost about $8. So we have enough money. Tell her that when we find an approximate answer, we are finding an **estimate**. $8 is an estimate of the sum of $4.85 and $3.39. Discuss other situations where an estimate would be useful.

- To estimate a sum or difference, we first round each number, and then add or subtract. Discuss the following:

$$943 - 281 \rightarrow 900 - 300 = 600$$

$$426 + 932 + 150 \rightarrow 400 + 900 + 200 = 1500$$

$$349 + 4569 + 920 \rightarrow 300 + 4600 + 900 = 5800$$

$$1250 + 801 - 30 \rightarrow 1200 + 800 - 0 = 2000$$

Tell your student she can use a wavy equal sign to mean "is about":

$$931 - 281 \approx 600$$

Point out that we usually round all the numbers to the same place value. Here we rounded them all to the nearest 100. Since we can easily add 3 hundreds + 46 hundreds + 10 hundreds, as in the third example, this gives a closer estimate to the actual amount than if we rounded the 4569 to one non-zero digit, or 5000. We could get an even better estimate if we rounded to the nearest 10, but then the calculations would not be as easy to do mentally. We want to get the closest estimate while still being able to do the calculations easily. There isn't one right answer in an estimation – the answer can vary depending on how close we want to come to the actual answer and how much computation we want to do in finding the estimate.

Have your student determine the actual sums or differences and compare to the estimates. (662, 1508, 5838, 2021)

Learning Tasks 8-11, p. 17

8. 1200

9. (a) 400 + 300 = 700 (b) 500 + 900 = 1400 (c) 900 + 700 = 1600
(d) 700 - 400 = 300 (e) 1000 - 300 = 700 (f) 1400 - 700 = 700

10. 1000

11. (a) 400 + 300 + 100 = 800 (b) 800 + 600 + 400 = 1800
(c) 800 + 200 - 600 = 400 (d) 1200 - 500 - 600 = 100

As a review of addition and subtraction, you may want to have your student determine the actual sums for these problems. He should be able to easily add 4-digit and 5-digit numbers to each other before proceeding to the next unit.

8. 1204

9. (a) 680 (b) 1399 (c) 1621
(d) 334 (e) 687 (f) 715

10. 1007

11. (a) 819 (b) 1800
(c) 435 (d) 120

Workbook Exercise 7

(4) Practice (p. 18)

- Practice concepts involving place value and rounding.

Practice 1A, p. 18

1. (a) 12,803 (b) 20,050 (c) 70,000

2. (a) one thousand, seven hundred fifty-eight
   (b) five thousand, three hundred six
   (c) seventy-two thousand, nine hundred three
   (d) ninety-one thousand, one hundred twenty

3. (a) 60 (b) 600 (c) 60,000 (d) 6

4. (a) 5980; 6080
   (b) 34,465; 35,465
   (c) 83,700; 93,700

5. (a) 30,016; 30,061; 30,160; 30,601
   (b) 20,990; 29,909; 29,999; 90,000

6. (a) 90 (b) 730 (c) 4620 (d) 9100

7. (a) 800 (b) 15,500 (c) 40,000 (d) 46,100

8. (a) 600 + 300 = **900** (b) 2200 + 900 = **3100**
   (c) 3900 + 200 = **4100** (d) 700 – 200 = **500**
   (e) 7100 – 200 = **6900** (f) 5400 – 200 = **5200**
   (g) 2600 + 100 – 500 = **2200** (h) 1400 – 900 – 300 = **200**

Part 3 Factors

(1) Factors (pp. 19-20)

 ➢ Understand **factors** using rectangular arrays.

Factors and multiples are important tools in working with fractions. A factor is a whole number. Any whole number greater than 1 can be expressed as the product of two factors. A number can be divided exactly by its factor, with no remainder. In *Primary Mathematics 3* the student learned the term **product**. Here the term **factor** is introduced. If your student cannot easily recall the multiplication and division facts, spend time reviewing them during this section.

 Give your student 24 **linking cubes**. Have him make as many rectangles as he can and record the results on graph paper (there is centimeter graph paper in the appendix).

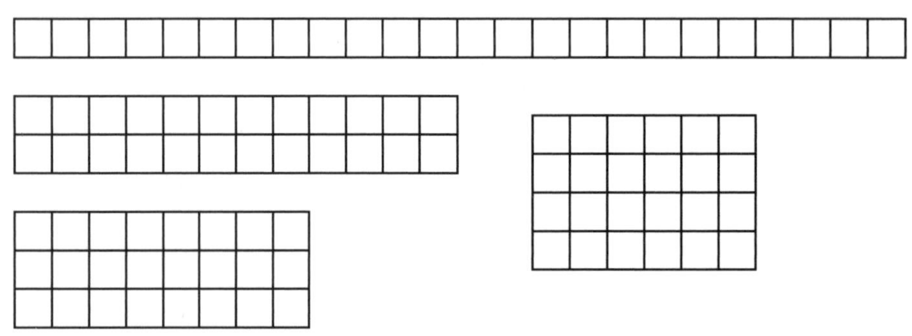

Write down the dimensions of the sides of the rectangles:

1, 2, 3, 4, 6, 8, 12, 24

Tell your student that these are the **factors** of 24. Factors are whole numbers. The factor of a number is one that the number can be divided by without any remainders. A number can be written as a product of its factors. In 2 x 12 = 24, 24 is the product, 2 and 12 are called the factors. A number can be written as the product of more than 2 factors. Help your student to find the ways she can write 24 as the product of 2 or more factors other than 1 or 12.

2 x 12 = 24	2 x 2 x 6 = 24
3 x 8 = 24	3 x 2 x 4 = 24
4 x 6 = 24	2 x 2 x 2 x 3 = 24

Ask: Is 5 a factor of 24? No, we can't make a rectangle of 24 squares with five on one side. 24 cannot be divided by 5 without a remainder.

Page 19
Learning Tasks 1-4, p. 20

1. 3 and 6; no; no
2. 1, 4, and 16
3. (a) 1, 7 (b) 1, 3, 9
   (c) 1, 2, 5, 10 (d) 1, 2, 3, 6, 9, 18
4. (a) 8, 10, 24 (b) 15, 20, 25

Workbook Exercise 8

(2) Common Factors (pp. 20-21)

- Determine if a 1-digit number is a factor of a given whole number.
- List all the factors of a given whole number up to 100.
- Find common factors of two whole numbers.

Your student should be able to determine if a number is divisible by 2, 3, 5, 6, 9, and 10 using rules of divisibility.

There are rules of divisibility by 4, 7, and 8, but they deal with larger numbers than 100 and are not taught here. They are given below for your reference. You may want to teach the divisibility rule for 4 during Unit 2.

4: Look at the last two digits. If the number formed by its last two digits is divisible by 4, the original number is as well. For example, 345**24** is divisible by 4, since 24 is divisible by 4.

7: To find out if a number is divisible by seven, take the last digit, double it, and subtract it from the rest of the number. If the result is divisible by 7, the number is divisible by 7. If you don't know the new number's divisibility, you can apply the rule again. For example, if you had 203, you would double the last digit to get six, and subtract that from 20 to get 14.

8: Check the last three digits. If the first digit of the last 3 digits is even, the number is divisible by 8 if the last two digits are divisible by 8. If the first digit of the last 3 digits is odd, subtract 4 from the last two digits; the number will be divisible by 8 if the resulting last two digits are. So, **23,888** is divisible by 8 because the digit in the hundreds place is an even number, and the last two digits are 88, which is divisible by 8. **23,886** is not divisible by 8 because the digit in the hundreds place is an even number, but the last two digits are 86, which is not divisible by 8. 23,728 is divisible by 8 because the digit in the hundreds place is odd, and 28 – 4 is divisible by 8.

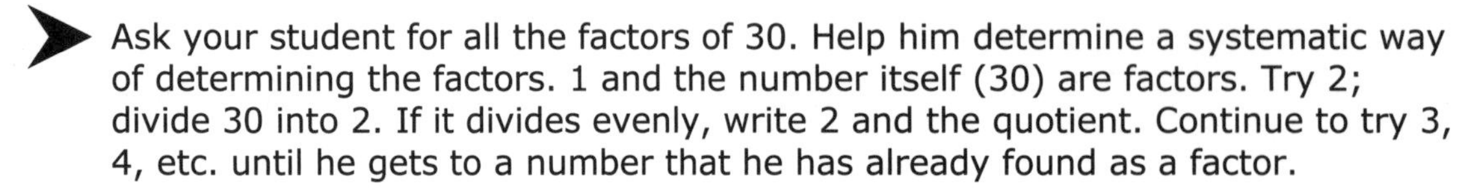

Ask your student for all the factors of 30. Help him determine a systematic way of determining the factors. 1 and the number itself (30) are factors. Try 2; divide 30 into 2. If it divides evenly, write 2 and the quotient. Continue to try 3, 4, etc. until he gets to a number that he has already found as a factor.

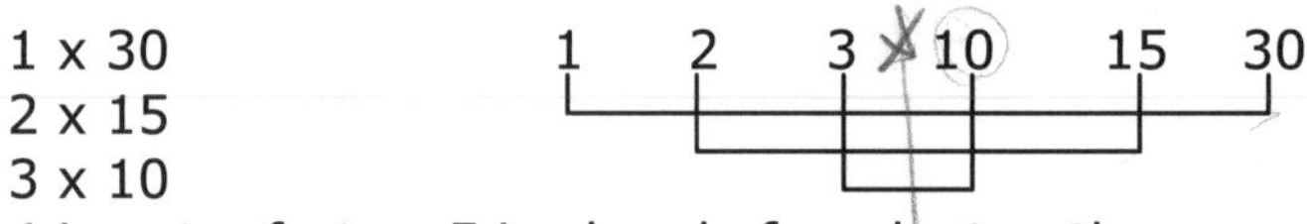

1 x 30
2 x 15
3 x 10
4 is not a factor, 5 is already found, stop there.

Rules of divisibility can be used to determine if a number is a factor of another number. These were introduced in the *Primary Mathematics 3B Home Instructor's Guides*. If your student has not done *Primary Mathematics 3B*, help him discover some rules of divisibility.

Use a **hundred-chart**. Have your student first circle or put a counter on all the numbers he lands on by counting by 2. (These are mutilples of 2, the term multiple is taught in the next section.) Ask him if he sees any patterns. Do the same with 2, 3, 5, 6, 9, and 10. Help him see the following patterns:

A number can be divided evenly by	If
2	It is even (the ones digit is 0, 2, 4, 6, or 8)
3	The sum of the digits of the number is divisible by 3.
5	The last digit is 0 or 5
6	The number is divisible by both 2 and 3
9	The sum of the digits of the number is divisible by 9
10	The last digit is 0.

If a rule of divisibility does not apply, use division to test if a number is a factor of a given number. Ask: Is 7 a factor of 81? No, 81 ÷ 7 = 11 r 4

➤ Have your student list the factors of 48 and 60 and find the factors they both have in common.

48: 1, 2, 3, 4, 6, 8, 12, 16, 24, 48

60: 1, 2, 3, 4, 5, 6, 10, 12, 15, 20, 30, 60

1, 2, 3, 4, 6 and 12 are common factors of 48 and 60.

- Which is the greatest common factor of 48 and 60? (12)
- Is 2 a common factor of 346 and 942? (Yes, they are both even).
- Is 3 a common factor of 681 and 804? (Yes, the sum of their digits is 15 and 12, so both are divisible by 3.)
- Is 5 a common factor of 634 and 10,565. No, 634 is not divisible by 5.

➤ Optional – Prime factors.

Give your student 23 cubes and ask him how many rectangles he can make with them. He will find he can only make a 1 x 23 rectangle. Tell him that a number that has exactly two different factors, 1 and itself, is called a prime number.

Use a **hundred-chart**. Have the student cover up all the numbers he lands on by couting by 2s (multiples of 2) excluding 2 itself. Then do the same for 3, 5, and 7. Note that numbers landed on when couting by 4s and 6s are already covered up. The remaining uncovered numbers: 2, 3, 5, 7, 11, 13, 17, 19, 23, 29, 31, 37, 41, 43, 47, 53, 59, 61, 67, 71, 73, 79, 83, 89, and 97 are called **prime** numbers.

Numbers that have more than two different factors are called **composite** numbers.

Is 1 a prime number or a composite number? It is not prime because it does not have two factors, and it is not composite because it does not have more than two factors. It is the odd one out.

Learning Tasks 4-13, pp. 20-22

4. (a) 8, 10, 24 (b) 15, 20, 25
6. (a) yes (b) no
7. (a) yes (b) yes (c) yes
8. (a) yes (b) yes
9. (a) 4 (b) 8 (c) 9
   (d) 9 (e) 7 (f) 8
10. 4, 8, 16, 32
11. 24, 16, 12, 8 8, 12, 16, 24
12. 1, 2, 4, 5, 10, 20, 25, 50, 100
13. (a) 1, 2, 4, 5, 8, 10, 20, 40
    (b) 1, 2, 5, 10, 25, 50
    (c) 1, 3, 5, 15, 25, 75
    (d) 1, 2, 4, 5, 8, 10, 16, 20, 40, 80

Workbook Exercise 9

Part 4 Multiples

(1) Multiples (pp. 23-25)

- Understand the concept of **multiple**.
- Relate the concepts of factor to multiple.
- Determine if a whole number is a multiple of a 1-digit number.
- List the multiples of a 1-digit number.
- Find common multiples.

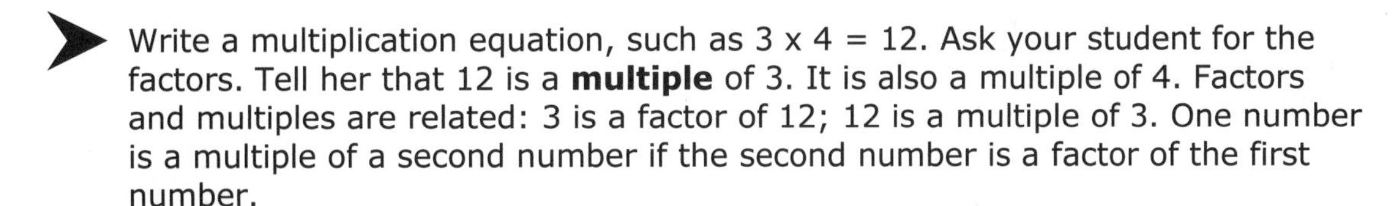

Write a multiplication equation, such as 3 x 4 = 12. Ask your student for the factors. Tell her that 12 is a **multiple** of 3. It is also a multiple of 4. Factors and multiples are related: 3 is a factor of 12; 12 is a multiple of 3. One number is a multiple of a second number if the second number is a factor of the first number.

Tell your student that the multiple of a given number is a number that can be found by multiplying the given number by any other number. When we list the multiples of a number, we list the product of that number and 1, then that number and 2, then that number and 3, and so on. Your student probably has had a lot of experience finding multiples. This is the same process as "skip-counting or "ladders" or counting by a certain number, such as by 3's.

Show how we can use the rules of divisibility to find out if a number is a multiple of another number. For example, ask your student whether 63 is a multiple of 3? Yes, because 63 can be divided by 3.

Use a **hundred-chart** and two kinds of counters, preferably transparent, or mark a hundred-chart copied from the appendix. Cover or circle all the multiples of 6. Cover or draw a square around all the multiples of 8. Tell her that the numbers with both kinds of counters or marks are common multiples of 6 and 8. Have her list the common multiples. Ask: What is the least common multiple of 6 and 8? (24) Can I find a greatest common multiple of 6 and 8? (No)

To find a common multiple of two numbers, we can find the common multiples of one of them, and then divide each multiple by the smaller number. The first one that can be divided evenly by the smaller number (no remainders) is a common multiple of both numbers. Show your student how to use this idea to find a common multiple of two numbers, such as 8 and 3:

> Multiples of 8: 8, 16, 24, ...
> 24 is a multiple of 3.

Ask your student if she can figure out an easy way to always find a common multiple of two numbers. The product of the two numbers is always a common multiple.

Page 23
Learning Tasks 1-11, pp. 23-26

1. (a) yes (b) yes
2. (a) no (b) no
3. (a) yes (b) yes (c) yes (d) no (e) yes
5. 9, 18, 27, 36
6. (a) 20, 24, 28 (b) 30, 36, 42
7. (a) 4, 6, 8 (b) 0, 5
8. yes
9. 24, 36
10. (a) 3, 9 (b) 18, 36

Factor game

Material: A **game board** of 4 x 5 squares with the numbers 2 through 15 and two stars written in the squares. (See appendix.) Two **dice**, one with the numbers 1-6 and one with the numbers 4-9 (Cover up the dots on regular dice with masking tape and write the numbers on the tape.) Two kinds of **markers**.

Procedure: This game is for 2 players. The players take turns throwing the dice to form a two digit number. The largest number is the tens, and the smallest the ones. The player then puts his marker on a number on the game board that is a factor of the number formed, if he can. If the number has no factor other than 1 and itself (it is prime), the player can put his marker on a star. If there are no suitable factors uncovered, the player must pass. The first player to get three markers in a row wins. If neither does, the game is a tie.

Multiple game

Material: A **hundred-chart** and either a **deck of cards** with the face cards removed (or a ten sided die). A different kind of **marker** for each player.

Procedure: Shuffle the cards and place face down. Players take turns drawing a card and placing a marker on a number on the hundred-chart that is a multiple of the number drawn. The first player with 3 in a row (or 5 in a row) wins.

Riddles: What number am I?

- I am less than 60. I am a common multiple of 10 and 15. (30)
- I am greater than 10. I am a common factor of 28 and 42. (14)
- I am a common multiple of 5 and 7. I am less than 100. I am not 35. (70)
- I am an even number less than 79. 5, 4, and 3 are all factors of me. I am a multiple of 10. (60)

Workbook Exercise 10

(2) Practice (p. 27)

- Practice concepts involving factors and multiples.

Practice 1B, p. 27

1. 1, 2, 3, 6, 9, 18

2. (a) 12, 15 (b) 25, 30, 35, 40

3. (a) 9 (b) 9 (c) 7 (d) 3

4. (a) 1, 2, 4, 8 (b) 1, 3, 5, 15 (c) 1, 2, 4, 5, 10, 20
   (d) 1, 2, 5, 10, 25, 50 (e) 1, 3, 5, 15, 25, 75
   (f) 1, 2, 7, 14, 49, 98

5. (a) 1 or 3 (b) 1, 2, or 4 (c) 1 or 3

6. (a) 2, 4, 6, 8 (b) 6, 12, 18, 24 (c) 8, 16, 24, 32

7. (a) 12, 24, 36,... (b) 20, 40, 60,... (c) 12, 24, 36,...

Unit 2 Multiplication and Division of Whole Numbers

Part 1 Multiplication by a 1-Digit Number, Division by a 1-Digit Number and by 10

(1) Multiplication by a 1-Digit Number (pp. 28, 30)

- Multiply a 4-digit number by a 1-digit number.

Students learned to multiply 2-digit and 3-digit numbers by a 1-digit number in *Primary Mathematics 3A*. If your student is not comfortable with the multiplication algorithm, spend some time with 2 and 3-digit numbers before going on to 4-digit numbers. If your student cannot easily recall the multiplication facts, spend some time reviewing them before proceeding.

Illustrate multiplication of a 4-digit number by a 1-digit number using **place-value cards** or **number discs**. A suggested procedure using place-value cards is given here. If using number discs, go through each of the steps with the discs, first multiplying the ones, renaming tens, writing down the ones below the line and the tens above the tens, etc., and showing the written steps at the same time. If your student thoroughly understands the multiplication algorithm, this concrete illustration won't be necessary. She can demonstrate her competence by simply working through the learning tasks. However, if there is still some uncertainty, concrete illustrations can help eliminate misconceptions.

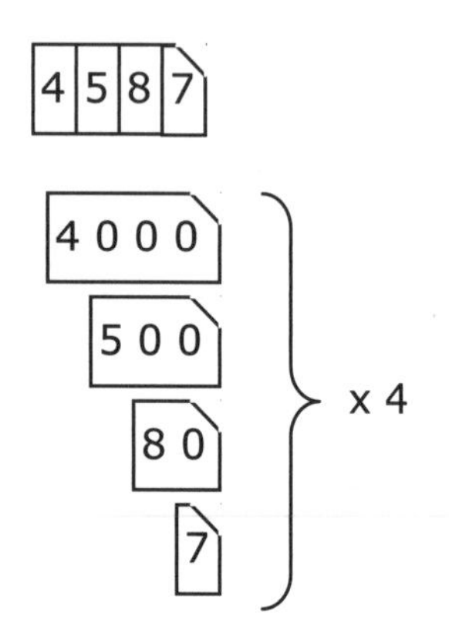

4587 x 4 is made up of 4000 x 4, 500 x 4, 80 x 4, and 7 x 4

$$\begin{array}{r} 4\ 5\ 8\ 7 \\ \times \quad\quad 4 \\ \hline \end{array}$$

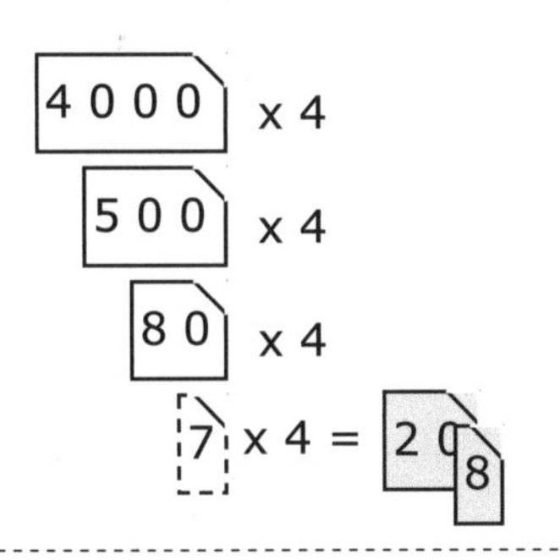

First, we multiply the ones by 4. What is the product of 7 and 4? (28) Will any of the other multiplications give a one? (No). We write the ones below the line, and a little 2 above the tens to remind us we have 2 tens already.

$$\begin{array}{rrrrr} & & & 2 & \\ & 4 & 5 & 8 & 7 \\ \times & & & & 4 \\ \hline & & & & 8 \end{array}$$

Now, we multiply the tens by 4. What is the product of 80 and 4? (320)

Will we get any more tens with any of the other multiplications? (No). We can add the tens and write that below the line.

$$\begin{array}{rrrrr} & & 3 & 2 & \\ & 4 & 5 & 8 & 7 \\ \times & & & & 4 \\ \hline & & & 4 & 8 \end{array}$$

We write 3 above the hundreds to remind us that we have 3 hundreds. We then multiply the hundreds with 4. What is the product of 500 and 4? (2000) We don't have any more hundreds, so we now write the 3 hundreds below the line.

$$\begin{array}{rrrrr} & & 3 & 2 & \\ & 4 & 5 & 8 & 7 \\ \times & & & & 4 \\ \hline & & 3 & 4 & 8 \end{array}$$

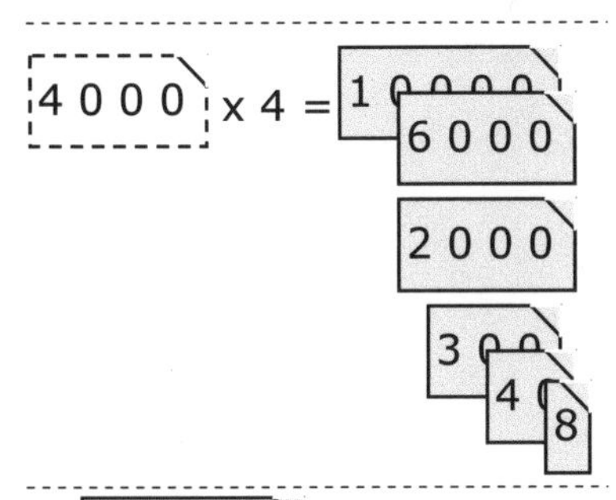

Now we multiply the thousands by 4. What is the product of 4000 and 4? (16000)

We add the 6000 to the 2000 we already have and write 8 below the line in the thousands column.

We then write the ten thousands below the line.

$$\begin{array}{rrrrr} & 2 & 3 & 2 & \\ & 4 & 5 & 8 & 7 \\ \times & & & & 4 \\ \hline 1 & 8 & 3 & 4 & 8 \end{array}$$

The product of 4587 and 4 is 18,348

Tell your student that when multiplying larger numbers, we should first estimate the answer so that we know our final answer has the correct number of digits.

Ask her to estimate 4587 x 4

4587 x 4
↓
5000 x **4** = **20**,000

By estimating first, we know the answer will be near 20,000.

Page 28
Learning Tasks 1-4, p. 30

2. (a) 17,700 (b) 25,960
3. 24,000
4. (a) 4000 x 5 = 20,000; 20,380
   (b) 4000 x 8 = 32,000; 34,536
   (c) 2000 x 9 = 18,000; 18,450
   (d) 7 x 7000 = 49,000; 48,517
   (e) 9 x 2000 = 18,000; 19,557
   (f) 6 x 4000 = 24,000; 23,040

Have your student do the following problems. Discuss the pattern that occurs when 9999 is multiplied by a 1-digit number? (Yes)

9999 x 1
9999 x 2
9999 x 3
9999 x 4
9999 x 5
9999 x 6
9999 x 7
9999 x 8
9999 x 9

Workbook Exercise 11

(2) Division by a 1-Digit Number (pp. 29, 31-33)

➤ Divide a 4-digit number by a 1-digit number.

The student learned to divide 2 or 3-digit numbers by a 1-digit number in *Primary Mathematics 3A*. If your student is not comfortable with the division algorithm, do examples with 2 or 3-digit numbers first. Your student should be able to easily recall multiplication and division facts.

Illustrate the division steps with **number discs** or other base-10 material. A suggested procedure is given here.

Set out a 1000-disc, six 100-discs, three 10-discs, and two 1-discs.

```
3)1 6 3 8          1638  ÷ 3
```

We start with the number in the highest place value. Can we divide one thousand by 3 and get any thousands? (No) Trade in the 1000-disc for 10 hundreds. Now we have 16 hundreds. Divide 16 hundreds by 3. Think of the highest multiple of 3 that is less than 16. It is 15. 15 ÷ 3 = 5. Put 15 of the hundreds into 3 piles of 5. We write the quotient, 5, or how many went into each pile, above the line in the hundreds place. We can write the number that we were able to divide up evenly (15 hundreds) below the 16 hundreds, and subtract to get the remainder, 1 hundred. (16 hundred ÷ 3 = 5 hundred remainder 1 hundred) We have now divided 15 hundreds by 3 and have 138 left to divide. Trade in the hundred for 10 tens. We now have 13 tens altogether to divide. We show that by writing the 3 tens next to our remainder.

```
    5
3)1 6 3 8          1638  ÷ 3
                     ↓
  1 5              1500  ÷ 3 = 500
    1 3             138  ÷ 3
```

Think of the highest multiple of 3 that is less than or equal to 13. It is 12. 13 tens ÷ 3 = 4 tens with a remainder. Put 12 of the tens into the piles, 4 in each. We write the quotient, 4 tens, above the line in the tens place. We can write the number of tens we were able to divide up evenly below the 13 tens and subtract to get the remainder, 1 ten. Trade in the remainder, 1 ten, for 10 ones. We are now going to divide up the ones. We can show we have 18 ones that by "bringing down" the 8 ones.

```
    5 4            1638  ÷ 3
3)1 6 3 8            ↓
                   1500  ÷ 3 = 500
 - 1 5              120  ÷ 3 =  40
     1 3             18  ÷ 3
   - 1 2
       1 8
```

Divide up the 18 ones into the 3 piles. Each pile gets 6. 18 ones ÷ 3 ones = 6. Write the 6 ones above the line in the ones place. There are no remainders. We can show this by writing the number of ones that we were able to divide up evenly below the 18 ones, and subtracting to show a remainder of 0.

```
    5 4 6
 3)1 6 3 8
 - 1 5
     1 3
   - 1 2
       1 8
     - 1 8
         0
```

```
1638  ÷ 3
  ↓
1500  ÷ 3 = 500
 120  ÷ 3 =  40
  18  ÷ 3 =   6
            546
```

Some students may develop a short-hand method of writing the division algorithm where they write only the remainder below. Writing all the steps is not necessary if they are not needed by the student.

```
    5 4 6
 3)1 6 3 8
    1   .
      1
```

Work through some problems that involve 0 in the quotient:

```
    905
 5)4526
   45
    026
     25
      1
```

Tell your student that, as with mutliplication, it is good to estimate the answer first to make sure that any steps were not forgotten nor place values lost. In division, we take the first two digits and round them to the nearest multiple of the number we are dividing by. Discuss the following:

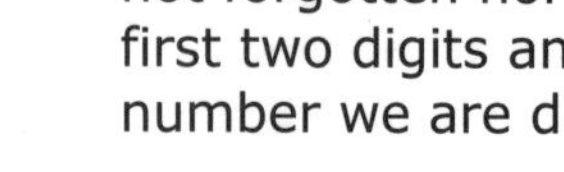

1638 ÷ 3	4606 ÷ 8	6923 ÷ 9
↓	↓	↓
1500 ÷ 3 = 500	4800 ÷ 8 = 600	7200 ÷ 9 = 800

Page 29
Learning Tasks 5, 6, 8-10, pp. 31-33

5. (a) 650 (b) 605

8. 600

10. (a) 3600 ÷ 9 = 400; 400 r4
(b) 3500 ÷ 7 = 500; 511 r3
(c) 3200 ÷ 8 = 400; 390
(d) 8000 ÷ 10 = 800; 812 r8
(e) 6000 ÷ 3 = 2000; 2509 r1
(f) 6000 ÷ 6 = 1000; 1196 r4

Workbook Exercise 12, problem 1

(3) Division by 10 (pp. 31-32)

➢ Divide by 10.

Use **base-10** material. Give your student 3 tens and ask her to divide them into 10 piles. She may try to trade in each ten for ones until she has 30 ones and then divide those up into 10 piles of 3 each. Tell her she can do it in steps. First trade in one ten, and divide the ten ones into 10 piles. Each will get one. Then do the same thing with the other two tens. How many tens came from each ten? The same number as the number of tens. Write

10 → 1 in each pile
10 → 1 in each pile
<u>10</u> → <u>1 in each pile</u>
30 → 3 in each pile

3**0** ÷ 1**0** = 3
3 ÷ 1 = 3

Now give her 3 hundreds and ask her to divide them into 10 piles. Tell her to do 1 hundred at a time. Write:

100 → 10 in each pile
100 → 10 in each pile
<u>100</u> → <u>10 in each pile</u>
300 → 30 in each pile

30**0** ÷ 1**0** = 30
30 ÷ 1 = 30

Give her 3 hundreds and 3 tens and ask her to divide them into 10 piles. Suggest that she first divide each hundred and each ten one after the other.

100 + 10 → 10 + 1 in each pile
100 + 10 → 10 + 1 in each pile
<u>100 + 10</u> → <u>10 + 1 in each pile</u>
330 → 33 in each pile

33**0** ÷ 1**0** = 33
33 ÷ 1 = 33

If a number ends in a 0, we can divide it by 10 by simply removing the 0, "sliding" the place value over one place.

Have your student do the following problems:

- 60 ÷ 10
- 400 ÷ 10
- 320 ÷ 10
- 8930 ÷ 10
- 4300 ÷ 10
- 6000 ÷ 10
- 23,980 ÷ 10
- 29, 100 ÷ 10
- 15,000 ÷ 10
- 30,000 ÷ 10
- 100,000 ÷ 10

Ask her how she would divide 3 hundreds by 100.

100 → 1 in each pile	
100 → 1 in each pile	3**00** ÷ 1**00** = 3
100 → 1 in each pile	3 ÷ 1 = 3
300 → 3 in each pile	

How about 3 thousand divided by 100?

1000 → 10 in each pile	
1000 → 10 in each pile	30**00** ÷ 1**00** = 30
1000 → 10 in each pile	30 ÷ 1 = 30
3000 → 30 in each pile	

And now, 3 thousand and 3 hundreds by 100?

33**00** ÷ 1**00** = 33
33 ÷ 1 = 33

This would be like sliding the place value over two places. With division, we can remove the same number of "trailing" 0's from both numbers and then divide.

Have your student do the following problems:

- 400 ÷ 100
- 4300 ÷ 100
- 6000 ÷ 100
- 29, 100 ÷ 100
- 15,000 ÷ 100
- 30,000 ÷ 100
- 100,000 ÷ 100
- 1000 ÷ 1000
- 43,000 ÷ 1000

There are additional problems in Mental Math 7.

Page 29
Learning Tasks 7, pp. 31-32

7. (a) 4 (b) 40
(c) 44 (d) 444

Workbook Exercise 12, problem 2

(4) Word Problems (pp. 33-34)

- Solve word problems of up to 3 steps.

In *Primary Mathematics 3*, students learned to represent word problems with pictorial models. Here, they will use the part-whole and comparison model to solve word problems of up to 3 steps. It is not necessary to model all problems, just those where a model would help in deriving the solution.

Part-whole model for addition and subtraction:

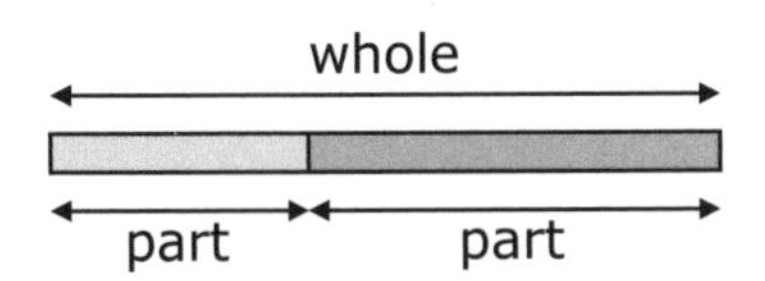

- ❖ Given two parts, we can find the whole by addition.
- ❖ Given a whole and a part, we can find the other part by subtraction.

Comparison model for addition and subtraction:

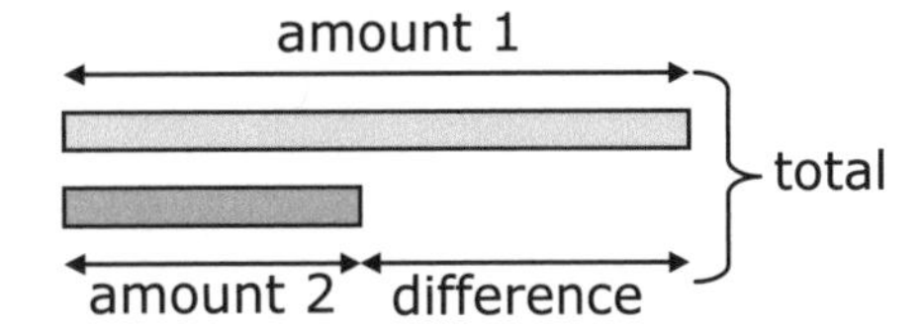

- ❖ Given amount 1 and 2, we can find the difference by subtraction.
- ❖ Given amount 2 and the difference, we can find amount 1 by addition.
- ❖ Given amount 1 and the difference, we can find amount 2 by subtraction.
- ❖ Once both amounts have been found, we can find the total by addition.
- ❖ Given the total and amount 1, we can find amount 2 by subtraction, and then the difference by subtraction.

Part-whole model for multiplication and division:

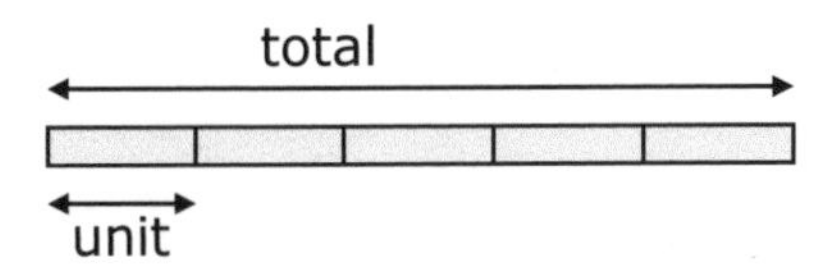

- ❖ Given the total and the number of units, we can find the value of a unit by division.
- ❖ Given the value of a unit and the number of units, we can find the total by multiplication.

Comparison model for multiplication and division:

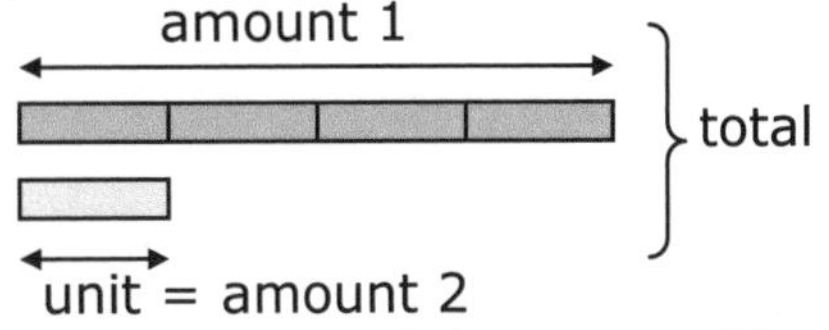

unit = amount 2

- ❖ Given the value of the unit and how many times as much amount 1 is compared to amount 2, we can find amount 1 by multiplication.
- ❖ Given amount 1 and how many times as much amount 1 is compared to amount 2, we can find amount 2 by division.
- ❖ We can then find the difference by multiplication or subtraction, and the total by multiplication or addition.

These models can be combined to illustrate more complicated problems.

- ❖ Given the value of a unit, the number of units, and a part, we can find the total by multiplication and then addition.
- ❖ Given the value of a unit, the number of units, and the total, we can find the part by multiplication and then subtraction.
- ❖ Given the total, the part, and the number of units, we can find the value of the unit by subtraction, and then division.

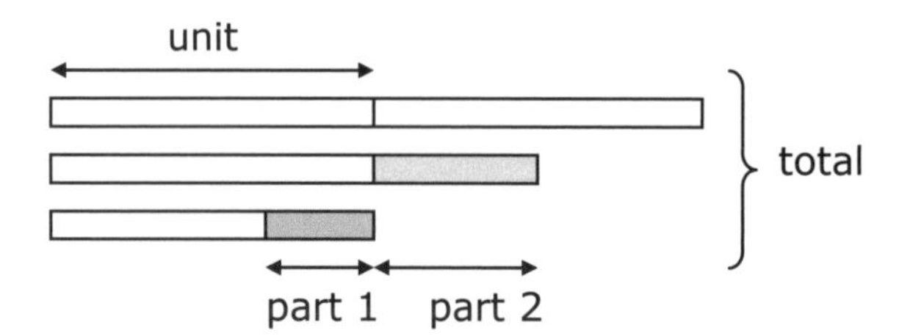

- ❖ Given the total and parts, subtract or add and then divide to find a unit. (3 units = total + part 1 – part 2)

Learning Tasks 11-13, pp. 33-34

For learning tasks 12 and 13, you may want to guide the student in modeling the problems. Methods can vary.

11. (b) 5445; 5445

12.

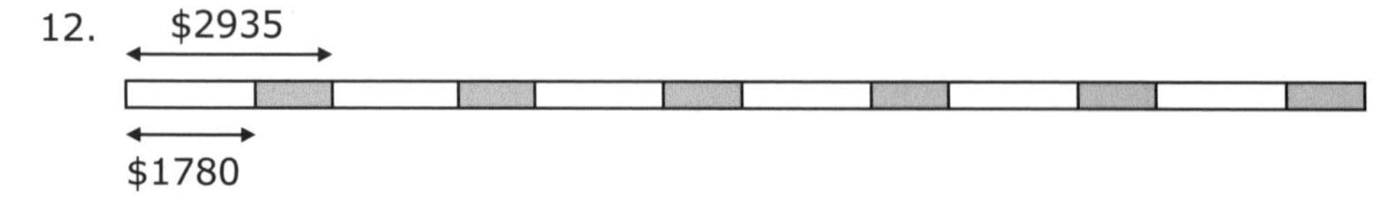

He saved $**6930**

13.

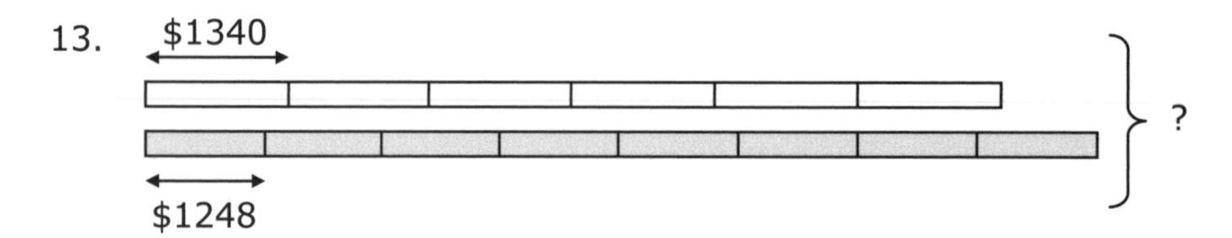

He spent $**18,024**

Discuss some additional problems involving comparison:

- John and Matt earn the same amount of money. If John spends \$130 and Matt spends \$480, John will have three times as much money as Matt. How much money does each earn?

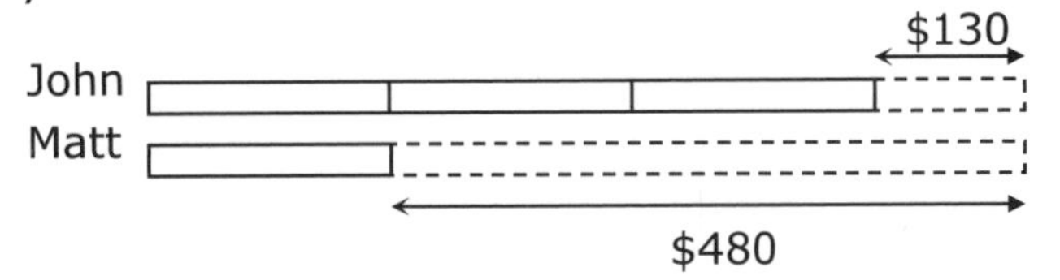

2 unit = \$480 - \$130 = \$350
1 unit = \$350 ÷ 2 = \$175
Amount Matt (and John) earns = \$175 + \$480 = \$655

- Amy has 34 stickers and Sara has 20. Amy gives Sara some stickers so they both have the same number of stickers. How many stickers does Amy have now? How many stickers did Amy give to Sara?

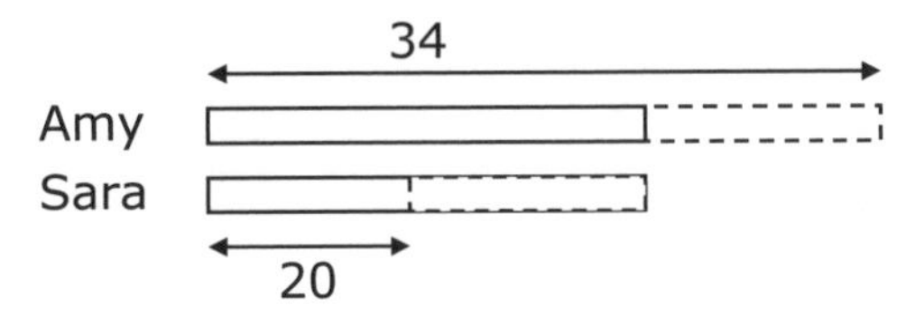

The total number of stickers does not change. Amy ends up with 1 unit, and Sara ends up with 1 unit.
2 units = total = 34 + 20 = 54
1 unit = 54 ÷ 2 = 27
Amy now has 27 stickers.
Amount she gave to Sara = 34 – 27 = 7
Or:
Amy has 34 – 20 = 14 stickers more than Sara. If she gives half of this, or 7, to Sara, they will have the same number.

 **Workbook Exercise 13**

(5) Practice (p. 35)

➤ Practice concepts involving multiplication and division.

Practice 2A, p. 35

1. (a) 6033 (b) 8428 (c) 17,250
2. (a) 25,290 (b) 27,419 (c) 56,322
3. (a) 703 (b) 1009 (c) 502
4. (a) 1202 (b) 496 (c) 909
5. (a) 918 r5 (b) 475 (c) 329 r9
6. Number of cakes sold this month = 1380 x 3 = **4140**
7. Cost of printer = $2560 ÷ 4 = **$640**

8. Number of rubber bands in 1 box = 1536 ÷ 6 = **256**
9. Number of bags of rice = 3750 ÷ 10 = **375**
10. Cost of 2 motorcycles
    = 2 x $3654 = $7308
    Cost of scooter
    = $9798 - $7308 = **$2490**

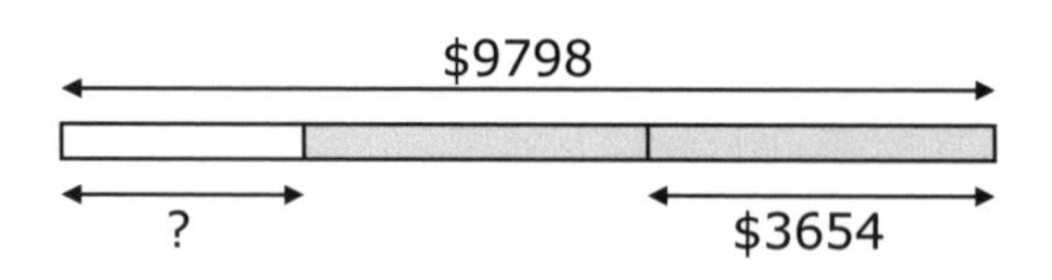

11. Amount earned in 4 months
    = $1895 x 4 = $7580
    Amount spent
    = $7580 - $3032 = **$4548**

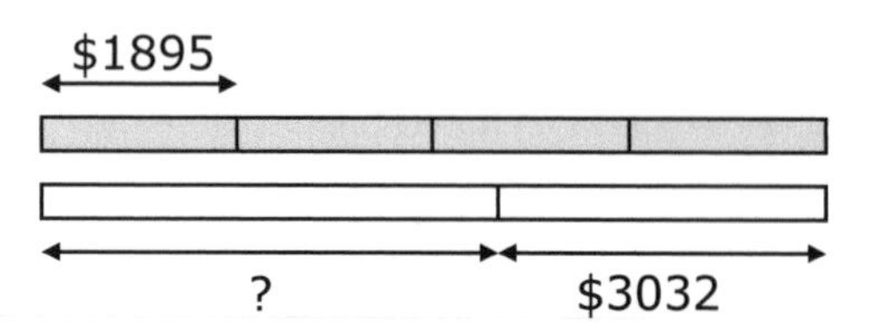

Part 2 Multiplication by a 2-Digit Number

(1) Multiplication by Tens (pp. 36-38)

- Multiply by a ten.
- Multiply tens, hundreds, and thousands with each other.

Page 36
Learning Tasks 1-2, p. 37

Illustrate the procedures on this page with actual **base-10** material, if necessary. A number can be multiplied by a multiple of 10 by first multiplying by 10 and then by the multiple, or by multiplying by the multiple, and then by 10.

1. (a) 160 (b) 400 (c) 2540
   (d) 290 (e) 960 (f) 3800

Discuss the following:

3**00** x 1**0** = 3 x 100 x 1 x 10 = 3 x 1 x 100 x 10 = 3 x 1000 = 3**000**
3**00** x 2**0** = 3 x 100 x 2 x 10 = 3 x 2 x 100 x 10 = 6 x 1000 = 6**000**
3**00** x 1**00** = 3 x 100 x 1 x 100 = 3 x 1 x 100 x 100 = 3 x 10,000 = 3**0,000**
3**00** x 2**00** = 3 x 100 x 2 x 100 = 3 x 2 x 100 x 100 = 6 x 10,000 = 6**0,000**
32**0** x 2**00** = 32 x 10 x 2 x 100 = 32 x 2 x 10 x 100 = 64 x 1000 = 64,**000**

We can take off trailing 0's, multiply the numbers together without them and add the same number of 0's back on to the product.
Try some additional problems:

4**0** x 6**0** = 24**00**
4**00** x 6**0** = 24,**000**
3**0** x 5**0** = 15**00**
3**00** x 5 = 15**00**
5 x 8**0** = 40**0**
5 x 8**00** = 40**00**
5**00** x 8**0** = 40,**000**

Note that the number of 0's in the product is the same as the sum of the number of 0's in the factors, with an extra 0 if the product of the single digits of the factors has a 0. Your student should be able to do these types of problems easily, as they will be essential for estimating multiplication problems.

There are more problems like this in Mental Math 8

Learning Task 7, p. 39

7. (a) 1200 (b) 4000 (c) 6300
   (d) 15,000 (e) 24,000 (f) 20,000

Discuss the following:

284 x 20

$$\begin{array}{rl} 284 & \\ \underline{\times\ \ 20} & \\ 80 & 4 \times 20 \\ 1600 & 80 \times 20 \\ \underline{4000} & 200 \times 20 \\ 5680 & \end{array}$$

$$\begin{array}{r} {}^{1} \\ 284 \\ \underline{\times\ \ \ 2} \\ 568 \end{array} \qquad \begin{array}{r} {}^{1} \\ 284 \\ \underline{\times\ \ 2\mathbf{0}} \\ 568\mathbf{0} \end{array} \qquad \begin{array}{r} {}^{1} \\ 284\mathbf{0} \\ \underline{\times\ \ \ 2} \\ 568\mathbf{0} \end{array}$$

Point out that when multiplying by 20, we can write a 0 down and then multiply as if we are multiplying by 2. It is as if we multiplied first by 10 and then by 2. So each place value is moved over one, and the number we carry, the 1 written above the 2, is actually a thousand. If this is confusing to your student, have her write out all the steps, as in the first problem above, in order to keep track of the place values.

Learning Tasks 3-4, pp. 37-38

If necessary, your student can rewrite these problems vertically.

4. (a) 690 (b) 4760 (c) 31,360
   (d) 1800 (e) 4050 (f) 33,600

Workbook Exercise 14

(2) Multiplication by a 2-digit Number (pp. 38-39)

- Multiply a 2-digit number by a 2-digit number.
- Multiply a 3-digit number by a 2-digit number.

Multiplication by a 2-digit number can be time consuming until the student gains proficiency through practice. As you go through the next unit on fractions, give your student several multiplication problems daily for practice. Watch out for common errors, such as not knowing the multiplication facts well enough, adding the renamed value before multiplying, instead of after, or not aligning the two partial products correctly.

➤ Tell your student that in multiplying larger numbers it is sometimes easy to lose track of the place value. To help determine if the answer is correct at least with regard to place value, we estimate. To estimate, we round each number to a multiple of 10, 100, or 1000. Have your student estimate the answer to some multiplication problems, such as

45 x 62 ≈ **5**0 x **6**0 = **30**00
394 x 2 ≈ **4**00 x **2** = **8**00
458 x 72 ≈ **6**00 x **7**0 = **42**,000

Remind him that the product must have at least the same total number of 0's as the two factors. There may be an extra 0 from the product of the two single digits.

➤ Write a multiplication problem, such as 67 x 54. First, estimate the answer:

67 x 54 ≈ 70 x 50 = 3500

Explain that 67 x 54 is the same as 67 x 50 and 67 x 4. We can multiply first by the 50, and then by the 4, and add, or first by the 4, and then by the 50, and add.

```
  67         67          67                    67
x 50       x  4        x 54                  x 54
3350        268        3350  = 67 x 50        268  = 67 x 4
    \      /            268  = 67 x 4        3350  = 67 x 50
     3618              3618                  3618
```

Learning Tasks 5-6, 8-10, pp. 38-39

8. 2100
9. 15,000
10. (a) 1000; 882 (b) 1400; 1512 (c) 3000; 2914
(d) 8000; 9476 (e) 24,000; 22,214 (f) 21,000; 21,920
(g) 25,000; 24,990 (h) 56,000; 54,234 (i) 54,000; 52,272

Multiplication Practice

Material: Playing cards with face cards and 10's removed, or 4 sets of number cards 1-9

Procedure: Shuffle and turn cards over. Each player draws 4 cards, forms two 2-digit numbers from them, and multiplies the numbers together. The player with the highest product gets a point. The player with the most points after all of the deck has been turned over wins, or the first player to get a certain number of points wins.

Challenge your student to find the pattern when 99 or 999 are multiplied by a 2-digit number.

99 x 11	999 x 11
99 x 12	999 x 12
99 x 13	999 x 13
99 x 14	999 x 14
99 x 15	999 x 15
99 x 16	999 x 16
99 x 17	999 x 17
99 x 18	999 x 18
99 x 19	999 x 19

Workbook Exercises 15-16

(3) Practice (p. 35)

- Practice concepts involving multiplication and division.

Practice 2B, p. 40

1. (a) 11,628 (b) 30,160 (c) 55,314
2. (a) 695 (b) 702 (c) 891
3. (a) 528 (b) 1769 (c) 5896
4. (a) 1313 (b) 15,317 (c) 61,308
5. Total copies delivered in 30 days = 165 x 30 = **4950**
6. Total number of stamps = 15 x 25 = **375**
7. Total cost of chairs = \$128 x 12 = \$1536
   Money she started with = \$1536 + \$342 = **\$1878**
8. If 50 is removed from the first group,
   both would have the same amount.
   2 units = 300 – 50 = 250
   1 unit = 250 ÷ 2 = 125
   There are **125** in the second group.

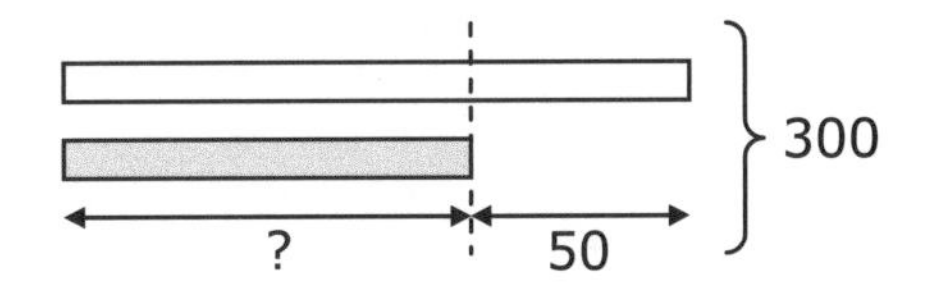

9. The larger number is 3 units,
   the smaller number is 1 unit,
   there is a total of 4 units, and the
   difference is 2 units.
   2 units = 2184
   4 units = 2184 x 2 = **4368**

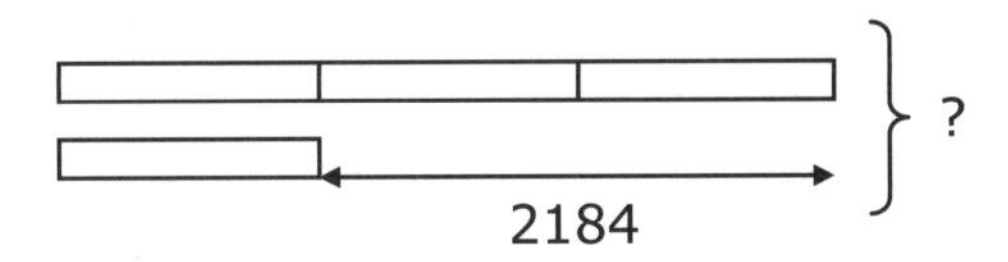

10. Amount saved in 15 months = \$65 x 15 = \$975
    Amount saved in the next 9 months = \$2001 - \$975 = \$1026
    Amount saved each month = \$1026 ÷ 9 = \$**114**

Enrichment 1 - Mental Math – Multiplication and Division

Multiplication by 1 digit can be done mentally using "front end" multiplication; multiplying by the highest place value first, and adding the partial products as you proceed.

46 x 3 = 40 x 3 + 6 x 3 = 120 + 18 = 138

First, multiply the first digit of the multi-digit factor by the single-digit number. Write the tens of the product down, remember the ones. Multiply the second digit by the single-digit number. Add the tens to the remembered number, write that down, remember the new ones Continue until all digits have been multiplied. Write down the last remembered number.

For example:

5276 x 3

5 x 3 = 15. Write down 1, remember 5.	5276 x 3 = **1**
2 x 3 = 6. 0 tens. Write down the 5. Remember 6	5276 x 3 = 1**5**
7 x 3 = 21. Add 2 to 6, write down 8. Remember 1	5276 x 3 = 15**8**
6 x 3 = 18. Add 1 to 1, write down 2. Write down 8	5276 x 3 = 15,8**28**

Explain this procedure to your student. More practice is available in Mental Math 9.

Students may also be able to divide by a 1-digit number without writing down all the steps. Divide each digit by the 1-digit number. The remainder is the ten for the next division

For example:

7824 ÷ 3

7 ÷ 3 = 2 r **1**. Write down the 2.	7824 ÷ 3 = **2**
18 ÷ 3 = 6. Write down the 6. No remainder.	7824 ÷ 3 = 2**6**
2 ÷ 3 = 0 r **2**. Write down the 0.	7824 ÷ 3 = 26**0**
24 ÷ 3 = 8. Write down the 8.	7824 ÷ 3 = 260**8**

Explain this procedure to your student. More practice is available in Mental Math 10.

Explain some alternate ways to multiply numbers close to a multiple of 10 or 100:

$39 \times 2 = 40 \times 2 - 2 = 80 - 2 = 78$

$39 \times 24 = 40 \times 24 - 24 = 960 - 24 = 936$

$99 \times 3 = 100 \times 3 - 3 = 300 - 3 = 297$

$99 \times 32 = 100 \times 32 - 32 = 3200 - 32 = 3168$

$399 \times 32 = 400 \times 32 - 32 = 400 \times 32 - 32 = 12{,}800 - 32 = 12{,}768$

Multiplication by 25 can be done by multiplying first by 100, and then dividing by 4:

$48 \times 25 = 48 \times 100 \div 4 = 4800 \div 4 = 1200$

$193 \times 25 = 193 \times 100 \div 4 = 19{,}300 \div 4 = 4825$

Some additional practice is available in Mental Math 11.

Review

Review A, p. 41

1. (a) 60 (b) 6000 (c) 60,000

2. (a) 24,038 (b) 74,002

3. (a) forty-two thousand, three hundred ten
   (b) fifteen thousand, two hundred six
   (c) twenty thousand, eight hundred fifteen

4. $2500

5. (a) 1, 2 or 4 (b) 24, 48, 72, 96, 120...

6. (a) 1600 (b) 10,000

7. (a) 342 (b) 833 r2
   (c) 712 (d) 314 r5

8. 3284 ÷ 6 = 547 r2 **547** in each package, **2** left over.

9. Total given to the children = 1240 – 80 = 1160
   Number of children = 1160 ÷ 8 = **145**

10. If 10 books were removed from the first pile, it would also have twice as many as the third pile.
    The third pile = 1 unit.
    The second pile = 2 units
    The first pile = 2 units + 10.
    Remove 10, and there are 5 units.
    5 units = 3000 – 10 = 2990
    1 unit = 2990 ÷ 5 = 598
    The third pile has **598** books.

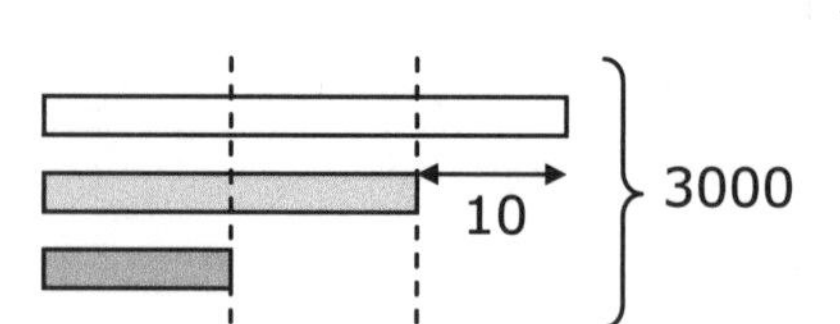

Workbook Review 1

Unit 3 Fractions

Part 1 Adding Fractions

(1) Equivalent Fractions

- Review fractions.
- Review equivalent fractions.
- Review comparing fractions.
- Review simplest form.

In *Primary Mathematics 3B*, students learned how to find equivalent fractions and the simplest form of a fraction. If your student did not use *Primary Mathematics 3B* or has not yet learned these concepts, you should teach this concept before proceeding. A review is included here.

In this section, all answers are less than 1. Like fractions have the same denominator.

Draw a fraction bar for thirds and shade one third. Tell your student that the bar stands for one whole, such as a whole cake or a whole tray of brownies. Ask them what fraction is shaded. Write the fraction. Remind her that the bottom number is called the denominator, and names the fraction (thirds) by telling us the number of fractional units that make up the whole. The top number is called the numerator and tells us the number of fractional units.

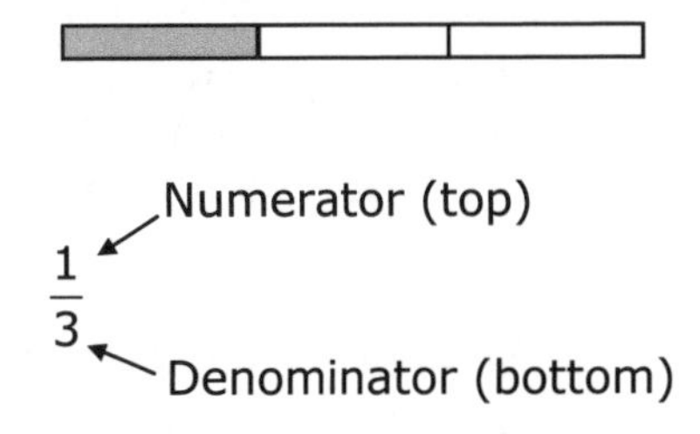

Ask her what fraction is not shaded. $\left(\frac{2}{3}\right)$

Ask her for the sum of the shaded and unshaded parts. Write the equation. Point out that we are adding all of the parts that the whole is divided into, so we now have one whole.

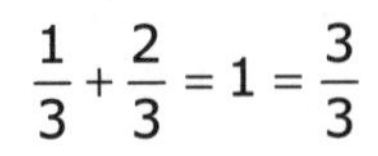

$$\frac{1}{3}+\frac{2}{3}=1=\frac{3}{3}$$

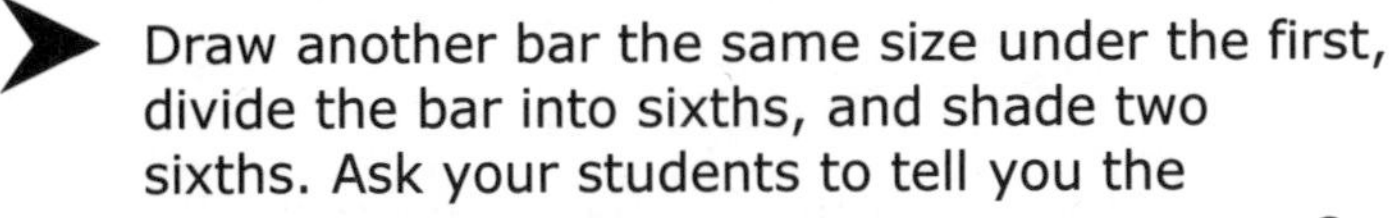

Draw another bar the same size under the first, divide the bar into sixths, and shade two sixths. Ask your students to tell you the fraction that is shaded. Ask him to compare $\frac{2}{6}$ to $\frac{1}{3}$. They are the same. Each part $\left(\frac{1}{6}\right)$ is half as big but there are now two of them.

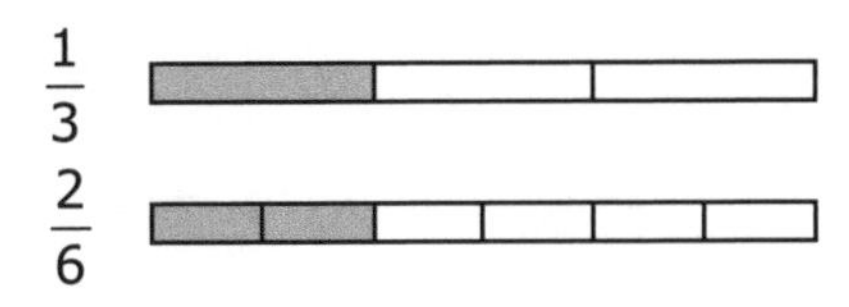

Ask your student if he remembers what these are called. They are **equivalent fractions**. Discuss how one can be derived from the other.

- We can multiply the numerator and denominator by the same number to get an equivalent fraction.
- We can divide the numerator and denominator by the same number to get an equivalent fraction.

You may want to illustrate another example, using fraction circles instead.

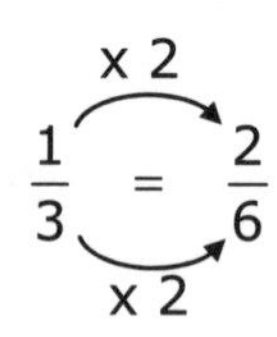
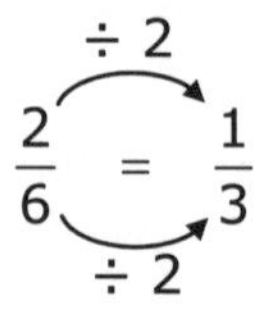

Write some fractions and your students find equivalent fractions.

Write two fractions with the same denominator but different numerators and illustrate with fraction bars. Ask your student to put them in order. Since the size of the fractional unit is the same, we put them in order according to the numerator.

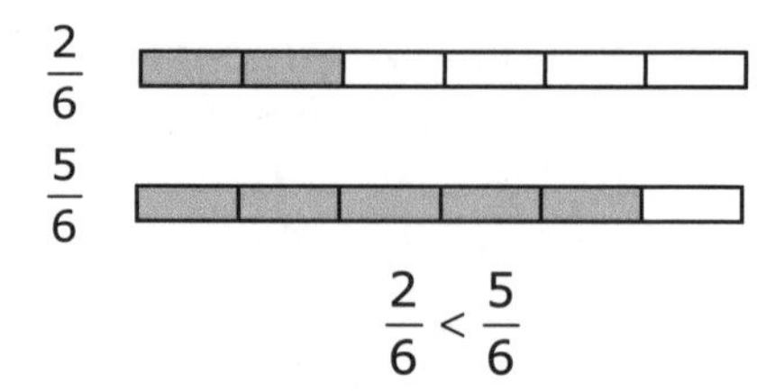

$\frac{2}{6} < \frac{5}{6}$

Draw fraction bars for thirds and sixths and shade one unit of each. Label the fraction. Ask your student which is smaller and why. $\frac{1}{6}$ is smaller than in $\frac{1}{3}$, because the whole is divided up into more parts and each part is smaller.

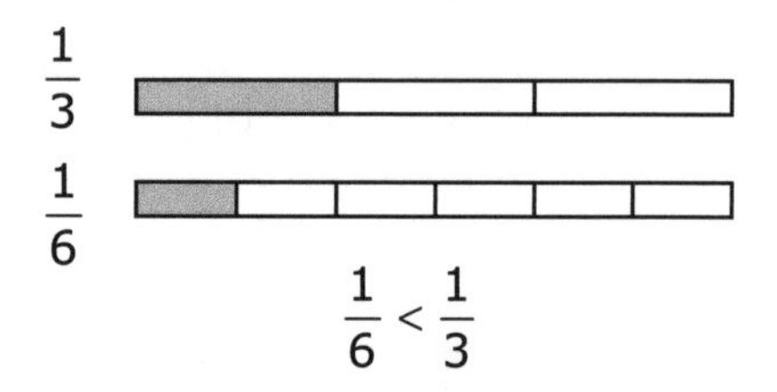

$\frac{1}{6} < \frac{1}{3}$

Shade another third and sixth and your students which is smaller, $\frac{2}{3}$ or $\frac{2}{6}$, and why. 2 smaller parts are less than two larger parts. If the numerators (number of parts are the same), then the fraction with the largest number in the denominator is smaller, since the parts are smaller.

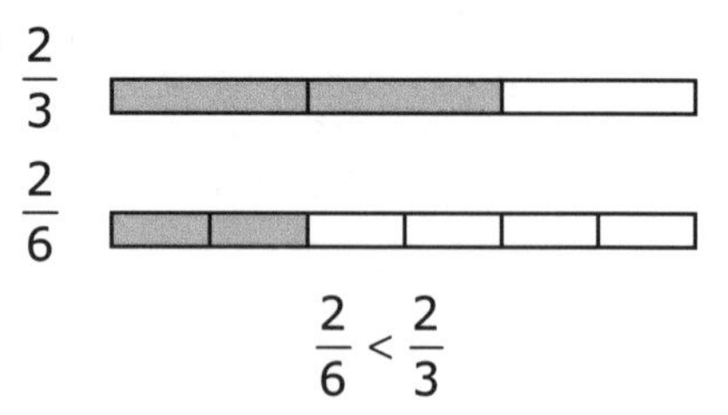

$\frac{2}{6} < \frac{2}{3}$

Write down 4-5 fractions with the same numerator but different denominator and ask your student to put them in order.

$\frac{3}{11} < \frac{3}{7} < \frac{3}{5} < \frac{3}{4}$

Write the two fractions $\frac{3}{5}$ and $\frac{2}{3}$ and ask your student which is smaller.

Remind her that if there are a different number of pieces, we can't compare them unless the size of the pieces are the same. Draw the fraction bars for these and ask for suggestions for making the size of the pieces the same. We can divide up the larger pieces (thirds) in fifths and the smaller pieces (fifths) into thirds so that each whole now has 15 equal-sized piece. The equivalent fractions $\frac{10}{15}$ and $\frac{9}{15}$ can be compared even without a diagram.

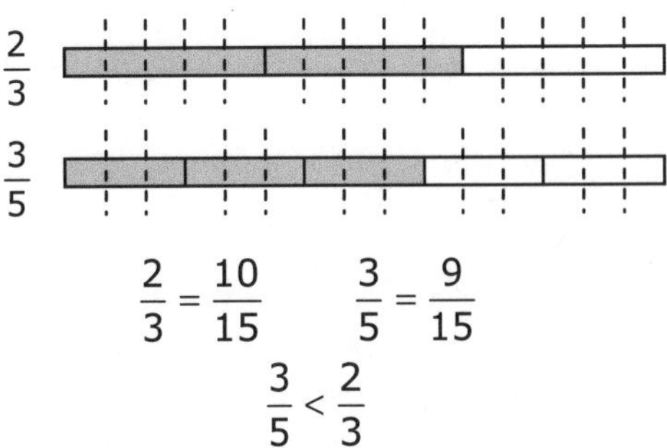

$\frac{2}{3} = \frac{10}{15}$ $\frac{3}{5} = \frac{9}{15}$

$\frac{3}{5} < \frac{2}{3}$

Write $\frac{5}{8}$ and $\frac{3}{4}$ and ask your student how we can compare these fractions. We can find equivalent fractions for both which have the same denominator. Then we can put them in order. Since the denominator 8 is a multiple of the denominator 4, we only need to find an equivalent fraction for $\frac{3}{4}$ with a denominator of 8

$\frac{5}{8}, \frac{3}{4}$

$\frac{3}{4} = \frac{6}{8}, \frac{5}{8} < \frac{6}{8}$ so $\frac{5}{8} < \frac{3}{4}$

Write $\frac{5}{6}$ and $\frac{7}{9}$ and ask students how we can compare these fractions. 9 is not a multiple of 6, so we need to find equivalent fractions for both until we get some with the same denominator. Point out that the equivalent fractions used could be any with the same denominator. We can compare $\frac{5}{6}$ and $\frac{7}{9}$ using $\frac{15}{18}$ and $\frac{14}{18}$, or using $\frac{45}{54}$ and $\frac{42}{54}$, which is obtained by multiplying one numerator and denominator by the denominator of the other fraction.

$\frac{5}{6}, \frac{7}{9}$

$\frac{7}{9}, \frac{14}{18}$

$\frac{5}{6}, \frac{10}{12}, \frac{15}{18}$

$\frac{14}{18} < \frac{15}{18}$ so $\frac{7}{9} < \frac{5}{6}$

Provide additional examples such as $\frac{2}{5}$ and $\frac{1}{3}$.

$\frac{2}{5}, \frac{1}{3}$

$\frac{2}{5}, \frac{4}{10}, \frac{6}{15}$

$\frac{1}{3}, \frac{2}{6}, \frac{3}{9}, \frac{4}{12}, \frac{5}{15}$

$\frac{5}{15} < \frac{6}{15}$ so $\frac{1}{3} < \frac{2}{5}$

Give students some fractions to put in order.

- $\frac{3}{7}, \frac{1}{7}, \frac{5}{7}$
- $\frac{1}{5}, \frac{1}{2}, \frac{1}{10}$
- $\frac{2}{3}, \frac{1}{2}, \frac{5}{6}$
- $\frac{2}{3}, \frac{1}{4}, \frac{5}{12}$

➤ Write $\frac{8}{12}$ and ask your student to find equivalent fractions using division. Show how you can find $\frac{2}{3}$ in two steps or in one step. Tell her that $\frac{2}{3}$ is an equivalent fraction that is in the **simplest form**. Simplest form is a term we use when there is no common factor that can divide both the top (numerator) and bottom (denominator) of a fraction. (If your student points out that we can divide both the top and bottom by 1, remind him that the fraction will stay the same.) As long as both the numerator and denominator can still be divided by the same number, the fraction is not in simplest form.

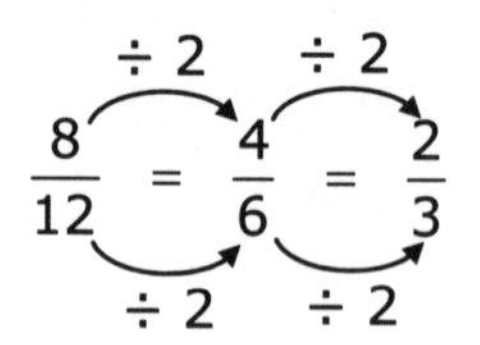

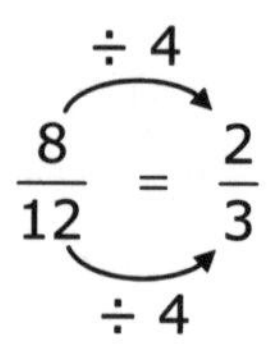

Write some fractions and ask your student to put them in the simplest form, or tell you that the fractions is already in its simplest form.

$\frac{2}{4}, \frac{2}{3}, \frac{6}{8}, \frac{3}{7}, \frac{6}{10}$

Write 5 numbers between 1 and 12 on the board. Ask your student to make as many fractions in their simplest form as she can using those 5 numbers.

2, 3, 5, 8, 9

$\frac{2}{3}, \frac{3}{5}, \frac{8}{9}$, etc.

(2) Adding Like Fractions (pp. 42-43)

- Add like fractions.

Like fractions are fractions with the same denominator. To add like fractions, we simply add their numerators: the denominator stays the same.

Page 42

Use fraction discs or fraction bars to illustrate the word problem here. Your student can color or shade the appropriate fractions if you are using ones copied from the appendix.

Learning Tasks 1-3, pp. 42-43

Help your student see that if the denominators are the same, then the size of the parts are the same, so the numerators (number of parts) can be added to get the sum. In Learning Task 2.(b), the sum $\frac{6}{8}$ is reduced to the simplest form $\frac{3}{4}$.

All answers should be in simplest form. Illustrate as many of the learning tasks as necessary with fraction bars.

1. 1
2. (a) 5 (b) 6; $\frac{3}{4}$
3. (a) $\frac{5}{9}$ (b) $\frac{4}{7}$ (c) $\frac{5}{6}$
   (d) $\frac{2}{3}$ (e) 1 (f) $\frac{4}{5}$
   (g) 1 (h) $\frac{2}{3}$ (i) $\frac{1}{2}$
   (j) 1 (k) 1 (l) $\frac{2}{3}$

Workbook Exercise 17

(3) Adding Related Fractions (pp. 44-45)

➢ Add related fractions.

Related fractions are fractions where the denominator of one fraction is a simple multiple of the denominator of the other fractions. To add related fractions we change one of the fractions into an equivalent fraction with the same denominator as the other so that both fractions can be added together.

Unrelated fractions are fractions neither of whose denominators is a simple multiple of the denominator of the other. For example, $\frac{1}{7}$ and $\frac{1}{5}$ are unrelated fractions. The addition and subtraction of unrelated fractions will be covered in *Primary Mathematics 5*.

Learning Task 4, p. 44

Tell your student that $\frac{1}{2}$ and $\frac{1}{4}$ are different sized parts. In order to add them, we need to make the part size the same. We can divide the $\frac{1}{2}$ into two parts of equal size so that we have $\frac{2}{4}$. $\frac{2}{4}$ is equivalent to, or the same as, $\frac{1}{2}$. We can add $\frac{2}{4}$ and $\frac{1}{4}$ by adding the number of parts, or the numerator, to get $\frac{3}{4}$.

Learning Task 5, p. 44

You may also illustrate this with two separate fraction bars to make the process a little clearer. Draw one fraction bar for thirds and color $\frac{2}{3}$. Draw another bar of the same length for sixths, and color $\frac{1}{6}$. Show the $\frac{2}{3}$ cut into equal size parts, giving 4 parts, or $\frac{4}{6}$. Combine the shaded parts.

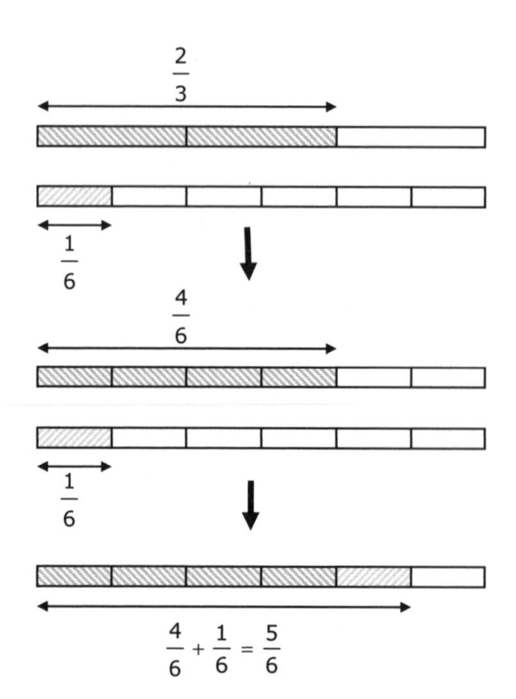

Learning Tasks 6-9, pp. 44-45

Illustrate problems with fraction strips, if necessary. All answers should be in the simplest form.

6. (a) 2; 5 (b) 6; 7

7. 2; 5; $\frac{1}{2}$

8. (a) 2; 3; $\frac{1}{2}$ (b) 5; 8; $\frac{4}{5}$

9. (a) $\frac{1}{2}+\frac{1}{8}=\frac{4}{8}+\frac{1}{8}=\mathbf{\frac{5}{8}}$

(b) $\frac{1}{4}+\frac{2}{12}=\frac{3}{12}+\frac{2}{12}=\mathbf{\frac{5}{12}}$

(c) $\frac{2}{3}+\frac{1}{9}=\frac{6}{9}+\frac{1}{9}=\mathbf{\frac{7}{9}}$

(d) $\frac{1}{2}+\frac{1}{6}=\frac{3}{6}+\frac{1}{6}=\frac{4}{6}=\mathbf{\frac{2}{3}}$

(e) $\frac{2}{5}+\frac{1}{10}=\frac{4}{10}+\frac{1}{10}=\frac{5}{10}=\mathbf{\frac{1}{2}}$

(f) $\frac{2}{3}+\frac{1}{12}=\frac{8}{12}+\frac{1}{12}=\frac{9}{12}=\mathbf{\frac{3}{4}}$

(g) $\frac{1}{5}+\frac{3}{10}=\frac{2}{10}+\frac{3}{10}=\frac{5}{10}=\mathbf{\frac{1}{2}}$

(h) $\frac{1}{6}+\frac{7}{12}=\frac{2}{12}+\frac{7}{12}=\frac{9}{12}=\mathbf{\frac{3}{4}}$

(i) $\frac{3}{4}+\frac{1}{12}=\frac{9}{12}+\frac{1}{12}=\frac{10}{12}=\mathbf{\frac{5}{6}}$

(j) $\frac{1}{3}+\frac{1}{9}+\frac{1}{9}=\frac{3}{9}+\frac{1}{9}+\frac{1}{9}=\mathbf{\frac{5}{9}}$

(k) $\frac{1}{2}+\frac{1}{4}+\frac{1}{4}=\frac{2}{4}+\frac{1}{4}+\frac{1}{4}=\frac{4}{4}=\mathbf{1}$

(l) $\frac{1}{4}+\frac{1}{8}+\frac{3}{8}=\frac{2}{8}+\frac{1}{8}+\frac{3}{8}=\frac{6}{8}=\mathbf{\frac{3}{4}}$

Workbook Exercise 18

Part 2 Subtracting Fractions

(1) Subtracting Like Fractions (pp. 46-47)

➢ Subtract like fractions.

Page 46

Use fraction discs or fraction bars to illustrate the word problem here, if necessary. Your student can color or shade the appropriate fractions.

Learning Tasks 1-4, pp. 46-47

Help your student to see that if the denominators are the same, the size of the parts are the same, so the numerators (number of parts) can be subtracted to get the difference. These problems can be illustrated with a part-whole model. In Learning Task 3 the difference $\frac{4}{8}$ is reduced to the simplest form $\frac{1}{2}$. All answers should be in simplest form. Illustrate as many of the learning tasks as necessary with a part-whole model where each unit is the fraction.

1. $\frac{1}{5}$
2. $\frac{7}{10}$
3. 4; $\frac{1}{2}$
4. (a) $\frac{3}{5}$ (b) $\frac{1}{8}$ (c) $\frac{4}{9}$
   (d) $\frac{1}{2}$ (e) $\frac{2}{5}$ (f) $\frac{1}{4}$
   (g) $\frac{7}{9}$ (h) $\frac{1}{10}$ (i) $\frac{5}{12}$
   (j) $\frac{1}{5}$ (k) $\frac{3}{8}$ (l) $\frac{1}{3}$

Workbook Exercise 19

(2) Subtracting Related Fractions (pp. 48-49)

- Subtract related fractions.

Learning Task 5, p. 48

Tell your student that $\frac{1}{2}$ and $\frac{1}{8}$ are different sized parts. In order to find their difference, we need to make the size of the parts the same. We can divide the $\frac{1}{2}$ into four parts of equal size to $\frac{1}{8}$ so that we have $\frac{4}{8}$. $\frac{4}{8}$ is equivalent to, or the same as, $\frac{1}{2}$. We can then subtract $\frac{1}{8}$ from $\frac{4}{8}$ by subtracting the number of parts, or the numerator, to get $\frac{3}{8}$.

Learning Task 6, p. 48

You may also illustrate these problems with two separate fraction strips to make the process a little clearer. Use or draw one fraction strip for eighths and color $\frac{7}{8}$. Use or draw another strip of the same length for halves, and color $\frac{1}{2}$. Show the $\frac{1}{2}$ cut into parts of equal size to $\frac{1}{8}$ giving 4 parts, or $\frac{4}{8}$. Then find the difference between the two shaded parts.

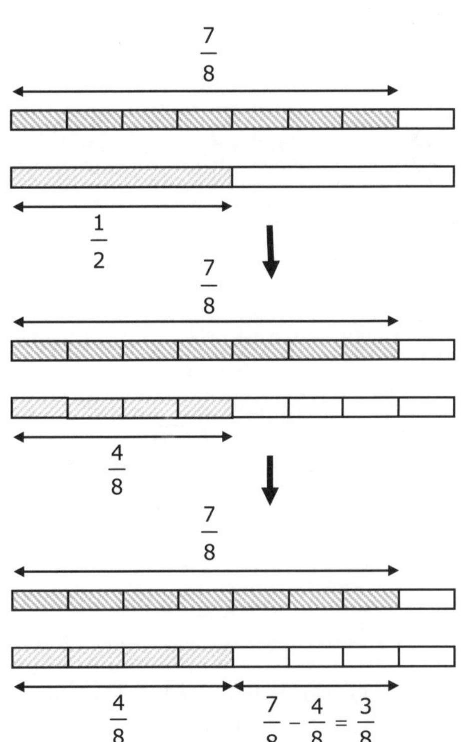

Learning Tasks 7-10, pp. 48-49

Illustrate each problem with two fraction strips or drawings, as necessary. Convert one into equal size parts, or the equivalent fraction, and find the difference. Or use a part-whole model, first finding like fractions. All answers should be in the simplest form.

7. (a) 6; 5 (b) 4; 3

8. 9; 4; $\frac{1}{3}$

9. (a) 5; 2; $\frac{1}{5}$ (b) 8; 3; $\frac{1}{4}$

10. (a) $\frac{5}{9}-\frac{1}{3}=\frac{5}{9}-\frac{3}{9}=\mathbf{\frac{2}{9}}$

(b) $\frac{3}{4}-\frac{3}{8}=\frac{6}{8}-\frac{3}{8}=\mathbf{\frac{3}{8}}$

(c) $\frac{4}{5}-\frac{7}{10}=\frac{8}{10}-\frac{7}{10}=\mathbf{\frac{1}{10}}$

(d) $\frac{5}{6}-\frac{1}{2}=\frac{5}{6}-\frac{3}{6}=\frac{2}{6}=\mathbf{\frac{1}{3}}$

(e) $\frac{1}{3}-\frac{1}{12}=\frac{4}{12}-\frac{1}{12}=\frac{3}{12}=\mathbf{\frac{1}{4}}$

(f) $\frac{7}{10}-\frac{1}{5}=\frac{7}{10}-\frac{2}{10}=\frac{5}{10}=\mathbf{\frac{1}{2}}$

(g) $\frac{1}{2}-\frac{1}{10}=\frac{5}{10}-\frac{1}{10}=\frac{4}{10}=\mathbf{\frac{2}{5}}$

(h) $\frac{3}{4}-\frac{5}{12}=\frac{9}{12}-\frac{5}{12}=\frac{4}{12}=\mathbf{\frac{1}{3}}$

(i) $\frac{5}{6}-\frac{7}{12}=\frac{10}{12}-\frac{7}{12}=\frac{3}{12}=\mathbf{\frac{1}{4}}$

(j) $1-\frac{1}{2}-\frac{1}{4}=\frac{4}{4}-\frac{2}{4}-\frac{1}{4}=\mathbf{\frac{1}{4}}$

(k) $1-\frac{1}{2}-\frac{1}{6}=\frac{6}{6}-\frac{3}{6}-\frac{1}{6}=\frac{2}{6}=\mathbf{\frac{1}{3}}$

(l) $\frac{2}{3}-\frac{1}{6}-\frac{1}{3}=\frac{4}{6}-\frac{1}{6}-\frac{2}{6}=\mathbf{\frac{1}{6}}$

Many students will be able to do simple addition and subtraction of related fractions mentally, without writing the intermediate steps. More practice is provided in Mental Math 13 and Mental Math 14.

Workbook Exercise 20

(3) Word Problems with Fractions

➢ Solve word problems involving fractions.

Since fractions are related to division, the part-whole and comparison models for multiplication and division can be used to illustrate word problems involving fractions. The bar is divided up into equal units, each unit being a fraction of the whole. To add or subtract units, they must be the same size, so the fractions must be converted into like fractions first.

It is not necessary for your student to diagram every problem. Models for fraction problems will become more useful later, as word problems become more complex, so they are introduced here. The problems in this section will be easily done without drawing a model.

Discuss the following problems with your student, demonstrating how to diagram them.

- Alice spent $\frac{3}{8}$ of her allowance on a book and $\frac{1}{4}$ on a toy. What fraction of her money did she spend? What fraction did she have left?

  $\frac{3}{8}+\frac{1}{4}=\frac{3}{8}+\frac{2}{8}=\frac{5}{8}$

  She spent $\frac{5}{8}$ of her money.

  $1-\frac{5}{8}=\frac{8}{8}-\frac{5}{8}=\frac{3}{8}$

  She had $\frac{3}{8}$ of her money left.

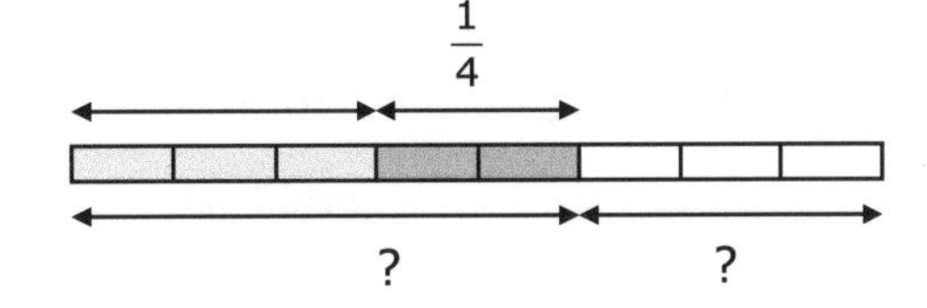

- Mrs. Shaw bought $\frac{3}{5}$ lb of meat and $\frac{7}{10}$ lb of fish. Which did she buy more of? How much more?

  $\frac{3}{5}=\frac{6}{10}$

  She bought more fish than meat.

  $\frac{7}{10}-\frac{6}{10}=\frac{1}{10}$

  She bought $\frac{1}{10}$ lb more fish.

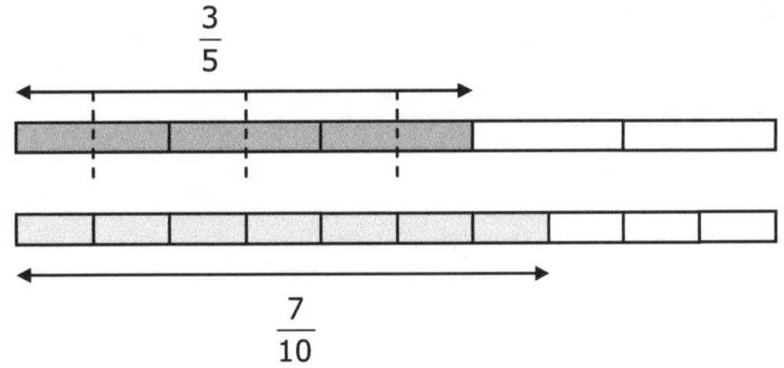

- $\frac{1}{2}$ of Bruce's marbles were red, $\frac{1}{4}$ of them were yellow, $\frac{1}{8}$ of them were green, and the rest were blue. What fraction of his marbles were blue?

$$1-\frac{1}{2}-\frac{1}{4}-\frac{1}{8}=\frac{8}{8}-\frac{4}{8}-\frac{2}{8}-\frac{1}{8}=\frac{1}{8}$$

$\frac{1}{8}$ of his marbles were blue.

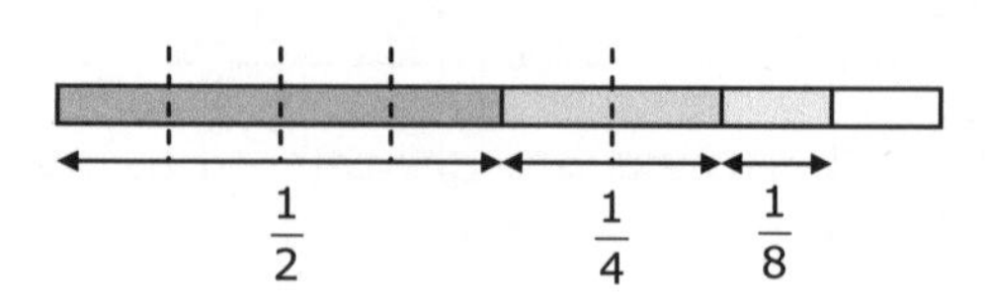

- How many $\frac{1}{8}$'s are there in $\frac{3}{4}$?

Draw a bar showing fourths, and divide each of the fourths into eighths. Count the number of eighths in three of them.

There are 6 $\frac{1}{8}$'s in $\frac{3}{4}$.

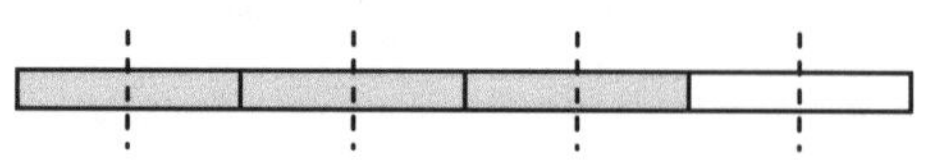

Fraction riddles:

- I am a fraction. My denominator is 8. But I am also a whole. What fraction am I? ($\frac{8}{8}$)
- I am a fraction. My numerator is a single odd digit. My denominator is a 2-digit number four times greater than my numerator. I am less than $\frac{1}{3}$ but greater than $\frac{1}{5}$. What fraction am I? ($\frac{3}{12}$)
- I am a fraction. When I am added to myself, I am equal to the sum of $\frac{1}{4}$ and $\frac{1}{12}$. What fraction am I? ($\frac{1}{6}$)

 **Workbook Exercise 21**

(4) Practice (p. 50)

➢ Practice adding and subtracting like fractions.

Practice 3A, p. 50

1. (a) $\frac{4}{5}$ (b) $\frac{5}{6}$ (c) $\frac{7}{10}$

2. (a) $\frac{3}{10}$ (b) $\frac{3}{7}$ (c) $\frac{7}{9}$

3. (a) $\frac{7}{8}$ (b) 1 (c) $\frac{7}{9}$

4. (a) $\frac{2}{5}$ (b) $\frac{2}{3}$ (c) $\frac{1}{2}$

5. (a) $\frac{3}{5}$ (b) $\frac{1}{2}$ (c) $\frac{8}{11}$

6. Total fraction eaten $= \frac{1}{8} + \frac{3}{8} = \frac{4}{8} = \mathbf{\frac{1}{2}}$

7. Fraction saved = total – fraction spent $= 1 - \frac{4}{9} = \mathbf{\frac{5}{9}}$

8. Fraction spent on racket $= 1 - \frac{3}{7} = \mathbf{\frac{4}{7}}$

9. Fraction left $1 - \frac{1}{6} - \frac{3}{6} = \frac{6}{6} - \frac{1}{6} - \frac{3}{6} = \mathbf{\frac{1}{3}}$

(5) Practice (p. 51)

➤ Practice adding and subtracting related fractions.

Practice 3B, p. 51

1. (a) $\frac{1}{8}$ (b) $\frac{7}{12}$ (c) $\frac{7}{10}$

2. (a) $\frac{5}{9}$ (b) $\frac{5}{6}$ (c) $\frac{2}{3}$

3. (a) $\frac{1}{12}$ (b) $\frac{1}{8}$ (c) $\frac{1}{2}$

4. (a) $\frac{7}{8}$ (b) $\frac{5}{12}$ (c) 1

5. (a) $\frac{7}{8}$ (b) $\frac{3}{8}$ (c) $\frac{1}{2}$

6. Amount left = $= \frac{3}{4}\ell - \frac{1}{2}\ell = \frac{3}{4}\ell - \frac{2}{4}\ell = \mathbf{\frac{1}{4}}\ell$

7. Total fraction used $= \frac{1}{2} + \frac{1}{8} = \frac{4}{8} + \frac{1}{8} = \mathbf{\frac{5}{8}}$

8. (a) Weight bought by **US›** Courtney **3d›** Mrs Chen:

$= \frac{2}{5}\text{kg} - \frac{1}{10}\text{kg}$

$= \frac{4}{10}\text{kg} - \frac{1}{10}\text{kg}$

$= \mathbf{\frac{3}{10}\text{kg}}$

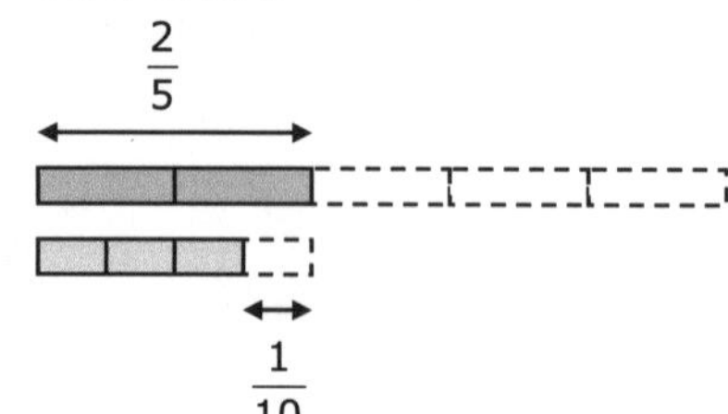

(b) Total weight = $\frac{4}{10}\text{kg} + \frac{3}{10}\text{kg} = \mathbf{\frac{7}{10}\text{kg}}$

Part 3 Mixed Numbers

(1) Mixed Numbers (pp. 52-53)

- Write mixed numbers.
- Add a fraction less than 1 to a whole number.
- Subtract a fraction less than 1 from a whole number.
- Determine the scale of a number line between two whole numbers.
- Locate mixed numbers on a number line.

➤ Use fraction strips or fraction circles or draw pictures. Show your student several wholes and several fractions, such as 2 wholes and 3 fifths. Ask him how he could represent this amount. Write $2\frac{3}{5}$. Tell him this is a mixed number. It consists of a whole number and a fraction. Write another mixed number and have him draw a picture to represent it. Discuss instances when mixed numbers might be used. For example, after a party $1\frac{1}{2}$ (one and a half) pizzas were left.

Page 52
Learning Task 1, p. 53

1. (a) $1\frac{1}{3}$ (b) $2\frac{3}{5}$ (c) $2\frac{1}{6}$

➤ Tell your student that so far we have been drawing number lines with whole numbers, and divisions between the numbers have represented a certain number of whole numbers. The space between two whole numbers, such as 1 and 2, can be divided up into fractions.

Use a **12 inch ruler** that shows 16ths between 0 and 6 inch marks and tenths between 6 and 12 inch marks. Show her that the longest line is drawn for wholes. Draw her attention to the interval between 0 and 1. Ask her what each next shorter division represents. ($\frac{1}{2}$). The next shorter line shows $\frac{1}{4}$. If measuring in fourths, the line at $\frac{1}{2}$ can be included to mean $\frac{2}{4}$ inches. Draw a line $5\frac{1}{4}$ inches long and have her measure the line and write the length as a mixed number.

Extend the discussion to the divisions representing eighths and sixteenths. Have her draw or measure some lines less than 6 inches to the nearest eighth and write the corresponding lengths as a mixed number.

Point out that the divisions between the inches for 6 to 12 inch are tenths. Have her measure some lines longer than 6 inches to the nearest tenth. Ask her how she would measure such lines to the nearest fourth.

Draw her attention to the other side of the ruler, with the centimeters. Ask her to draw a line $11\frac{1}{2}$ cm long, or $6\frac{3}{10}$ cm long.

Learning Task 2, p. 53

2. (a) A - $1\frac{4}{5}$ B - $2\frac{4}{5}$

   (b) C - $1\frac{3}{8}$ D - $1\frac{7}{8}$

Draw 3 whole circles or bars. Ask your student to take away $\frac{1}{5}$. Point out that she has taken it away from one of the wholes.

Write $3 - \frac{1}{5} = 2 + 1 - \frac{1}{5} = 2\frac{4}{5}$.

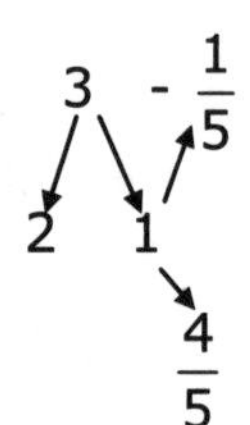

She can subtract a fraction from a whole number larger than 1 by subtracting it from a one, giving one less whole and the difference between one and that fraction.

Learning Task 3 p. 53

3. (a) $3\frac{2}{3}$ (b) $2\frac{4}{5}$ (c) $4\frac{7}{10}$

   (d) $1\frac{3}{4}$ (e) $2\frac{4}{5}$ (f) $4\frac{1}{3}$

Workbook Exercise 22

Enrichment 2 - Mental Math - Subtracting a Mixed Number from a Whole Number

A fraction less than one can be subtracted from a whole number by subtracting from one of the ones.

$$3-\frac{1}{5}=2\frac{4}{5}$$

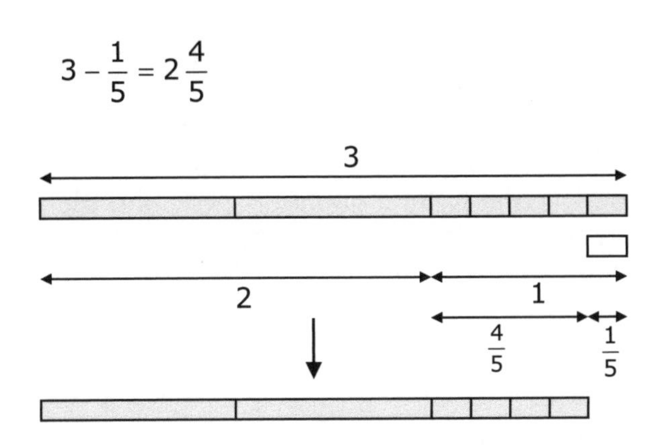

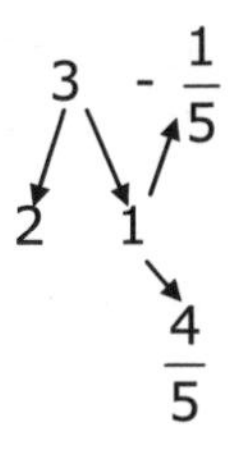

A mixed number can be subtracted from a whole number by first subtracting the whole number part of the mixed number, then the fraction part.

$$5-3\frac{1}{3}=1\frac{2}{3} \qquad 5-3\frac{1}{3}=2-\frac{1}{3}=1\frac{2}{3}$$

Use fraction bars or drawings to illustrate this concept to your student. Mental Math 15 has more practice.

Part 4 Improper Fractions

(1) Improper Fractions (pp. 54-55)

- Interpret improper fractions as multiples of unit fractions.
- Define improper fractions as a fraction whose numerator is equal to or greater than the denominator.
- Understand the relationship between improper fractions and mixed numbers.

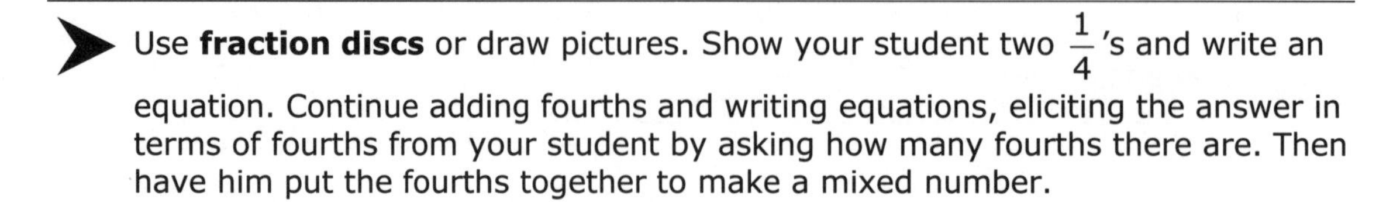

Use **fraction discs** or draw pictures. Show your student two $\frac{1}{4}$'s and write an equation. Continue adding fourths and writing equations, eliciting the answer in terms of fourths from your student by asking how many fourths there are. Then have him put the fourths together to make a mixed number.

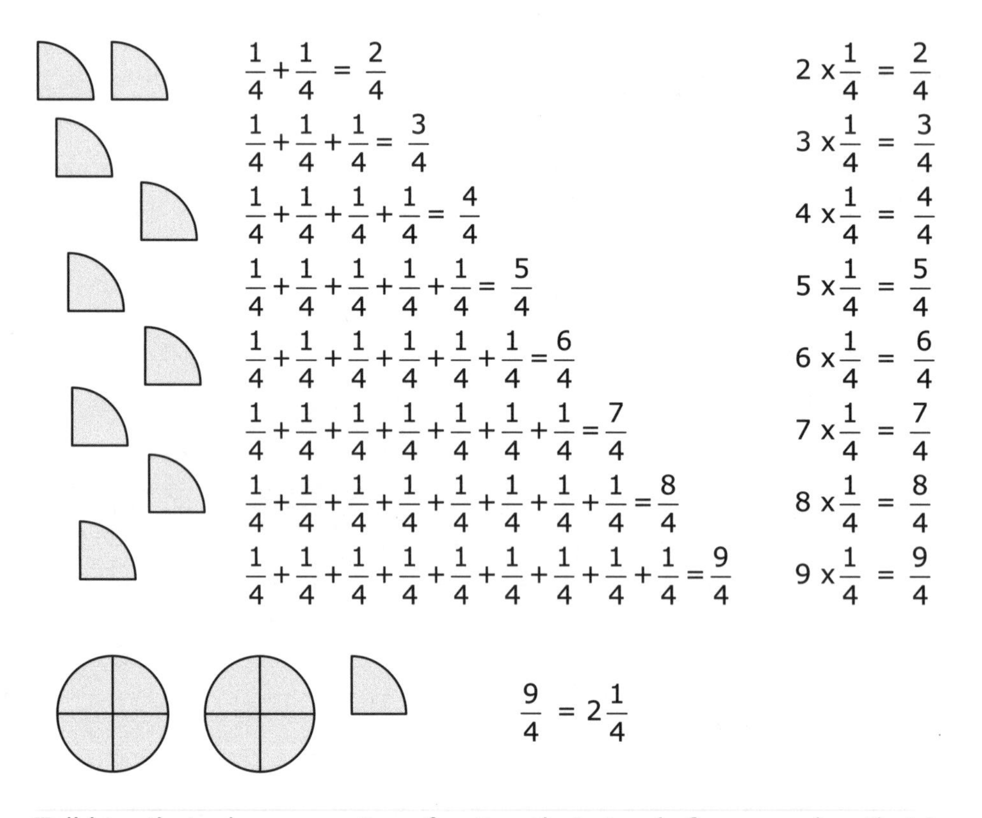

$\frac{1}{4}+\frac{1}{4}=\frac{2}{4}$ $\quad 2\times\frac{1}{4}=\frac{2}{4}$

$\frac{1}{4}+\frac{1}{4}+\frac{1}{4}=\frac{3}{4}$ $\quad 3\times\frac{1}{4}=\frac{3}{4}$

$\frac{1}{4}+\frac{1}{4}+\frac{1}{4}+\frac{1}{4}=\frac{4}{4}$ $\quad 4\times\frac{1}{4}=\frac{4}{4}$

$\frac{1}{4}+\frac{1}{4}+\frac{1}{4}+\frac{1}{4}+\frac{1}{4}=\frac{5}{4}$ $\quad 5\times\frac{1}{4}=\frac{5}{4}$

$\frac{1}{4}+\frac{1}{4}+\frac{1}{4}+\frac{1}{4}+\frac{1}{4}+\frac{1}{4}=\frac{6}{4}$ $\quad 6\times\frac{1}{4}=\frac{6}{4}$

$\frac{1}{4}+\frac{1}{4}+\frac{1}{4}+\frac{1}{4}+\frac{1}{4}+\frac{1}{4}+\frac{1}{4}=\frac{7}{4}$ $\quad 7\times\frac{1}{4}=\frac{7}{4}$

$\frac{1}{4}+\frac{1}{4}+\frac{1}{4}+\frac{1}{4}+\frac{1}{4}+\frac{1}{4}+\frac{1}{4}+\frac{1}{4}=\frac{8}{4}$ $\quad 8\times\frac{1}{4}=\frac{8}{4}$

$\frac{1}{4}+\frac{1}{4}+\frac{1}{4}+\frac{1}{4}+\frac{1}{4}+\frac{1}{4}+\frac{1}{4}+\frac{1}{4}+\frac{1}{4}=\frac{9}{4}$ $\quad 9\times\frac{1}{4}=\frac{9}{4}$

$\frac{9}{4}=2\frac{1}{4}$

Tell him that when we write a fraction that stands for a number that is equal to or greater than a whole, we call it an **improper fraction**. $\frac{4}{4}$, $\frac{5}{4}$, $\frac{6}{4}$, $\frac{7}{4}$, $\frac{8}{4}$ and $\frac{9}{4}$ are improper fractions. The term fraction means part of a whole. If they are bigger than a whole, then they are not really part of a whole, thus they are *improper*. Ask him how we can recognize improper fractions by looking at the numerator and denominator. The numerator is equal to or larger than the denominator.

Learning Tasks 1-2, p. 55

1. 7
2. (a) $\frac{5}{5}$ (b) $\frac{7}{4}$ (c) $\frac{12}{6}$

Workbook Exercise 23

(2) Converting Improper Fractions to Mixed Numbers (p. 56)

- Convert an improper fraction to a mixed number.

Discuss ways to change an improper fraction into a mixed number. Write an improper fraction such as $\frac{17}{5}$. Use **fraction discs** or diagrams to illustrate.

Your student can make wholes one at a time, such as

$\frac{17}{5} = 1\frac{12}{5}$ Use 5 fifths to make a whole; this leaves 17 - 5 = 12 fifths.

$\frac{17}{5} = 1\frac{12}{5} = 2\frac{7}{5}$ Use another 5 fifths for a whole, this leaves 7 fifths.

$\frac{17}{5} = 1\frac{12}{5} = 2\frac{7}{5} = 3\frac{2}{5}$ Make a third whole, leaving only 2 fifths.

We put 3 x 5 fifths = 15 fifths into wholes. 15 is a multiple of 5 closest to 17. So the fraction can be broken up into two fractions, one with 15 of the fifths, and the other with the remaining 2 fifths:

$\frac{17}{5} = \frac{15}{5} + \frac{2}{5} = 3\frac{2}{5}$

Your student may see the similarity of this to division with a remainder. 17 ÷ 5 = 3 r 2. If so, he can use this idea. The relationship between fractions and division will be further explored in *Primary Mathematics 5A*.

Learning Tasks 3-5, p. 56

3. (a) 2 (b) $2\frac{4}{5}$

4. $2\frac{1}{6}$

5. (a) $4\frac{1}{4}$ (b) $3\frac{1}{3}$ (c) 4 (d) $2\frac{2}{5}$

Workbook Exercise 24

(3) Converting Mixed Numbers to Improper Fractions (pp. 56-57)

➢ Convert a mixed number to an improper fraction.

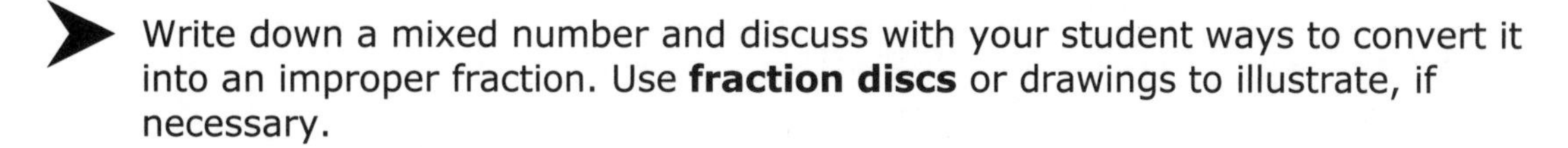

➤ Write down a mixed number and discuss with your student ways to convert it into an improper fraction. Use **fraction discs** or drawings to illustrate, if necessary.

For example, we can convert each whole number into an improper fraction and add them together. Draw two whole discs and $\frac{2}{5}$ of a disc and write

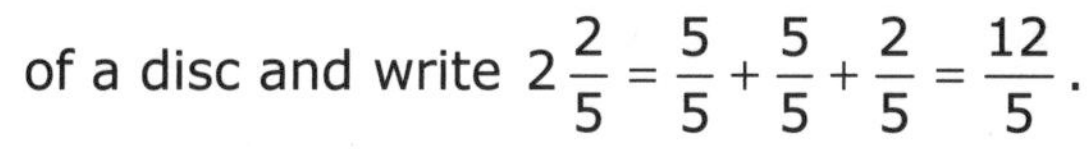

$2\frac{2}{5} = \frac{5}{5} + \frac{5}{5} + \frac{2}{5} = \frac{12}{5}$.

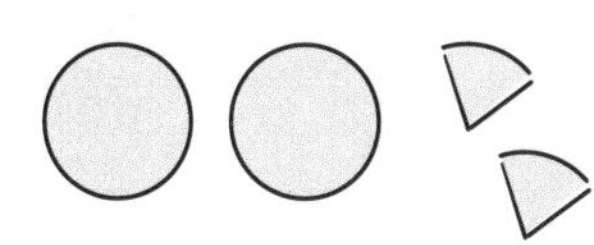

Point out that we can skip a step by making a mixed number of the 2 right away. Divide up each whole disk into fifths and write $2\frac{2}{5} = \frac{10}{5} + \frac{2}{5} = \frac{12}{5}$. The numerator in $\frac{10}{5}$ is two times the number of parts we are dividing up each whole into, or 5.

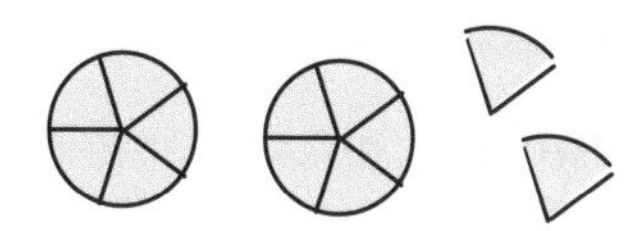

You can also illustrate this using fraction bars or drawing of fraction bars, lining them up as in a number line, and cutting each whole bar into fractions:

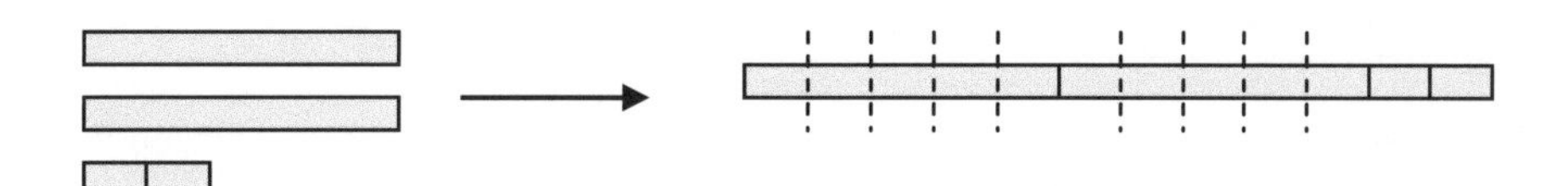

Remind your student that if the numerator is a multiple of the denominator, the fraction is equivalent to a whole number. Do other examples as necessary.

➤ As your student goes through the learning tasks for this section, see if she can discover a short-cut method. We can multiply the whole number by the denominator of the fraction and add the numerator to get the numerator of the improper fraction: $2\frac{2}{5} = \frac{2 \times 5 + 2}{5} = \frac{12}{5}$. Make sure she understands why this works. She can do this step mentally.

Learning Tasks 6-9, pp. 56-57

In learning task 9, only one of the wholes is being used to make the improper fraction.

6. (a) 11 (b) $\frac{21}{8}$
7. $\frac{19}{6}$
8. (a) $\frac{9}{5}$ (b) $\frac{8}{3}$
   (c) $\frac{9}{4}$ (d) $\frac{17}{6}$
9. (a) 4 (b) 7 (c) 5
   (d) 3 (e) 7 (f) 7

Workbook Exercise 25

(4) Adding and Subtracting Fractions (p. 57)

- Add and subtract fractions involving improper fractions.

Discuss with your student ways to add fractions where the result can be an improper fraction. The final answer should be given as a mixed fraction.

The two fractions can be added together, giving an improper fraction, which is converted into a mixed number:

$$\frac{5}{7}+\frac{4}{7}=\frac{9}{7}=1\frac{2}{7}$$

Or, we can "make a whole." Determine how much needs to be added to the numerator of one of the fractions so that it equals the denominator, making a whole. Subtract that from the numerator of the second fraction.

2

$$\frac{5}{7}+\frac{4}{7}=\frac{7}{7}+\frac{2}{7}=1\frac{2}{7}$$

To add unlike fractions, we must first convert them into like fractions. We can then use either method to add them together.

$$\frac{7}{8}+\frac{3}{4}=\frac{7}{8}+\frac{6}{8}=\frac{13}{8}=1\frac{5}{8}$$

1

$$\frac{7}{8}+\frac{3}{4}=\frac{7}{8}+\frac{6}{8}=1\frac{5}{8}$$

Provide other examples as necessary. The second method is easier for mental addition. More practice is provided in Mental Math 16 in the appendix. (Your student may have to write an intermediate step for some of these problems.)

Subtracting a fraction from whole numbers has already been discussed in an earlier section.

$$4-\frac{2}{5}=3+1-\frac{2}{5}=3+\frac{5}{5}-\frac{2}{5}=3\frac{3}{5}$$

Learning Tasks 10-12, p. 57

10. (a) $2\frac{1}{2}$ (b) 4 (c) $2\frac{1}{2}$ (d) $2\frac{2}{3}$
    (e) $3\frac{3}{5}$ (f) $4\frac{3}{4}$ (g) $1\frac{3}{4}$ (h) 4

11. (a) $1\frac{2}{3}$ (b) $1\frac{2}{5}$ (c) 1
    (d) $1\frac{4}{7}$ (e) $1\frac{1}{2}$ (f) $1\frac{5}{8}$

12. (a) $2\frac{1}{4}$ (b) $1\frac{5}{8}$ (c) $3\frac{1}{2}$
    (d) $1\frac{7}{10}$ (e) $1\frac{1}{5}$ (f) $2\frac{2}{7}$

Workbook Exercise 26
Workbook Review 2

Part 5 Fractions of a Set

(1) The Fraction of a Set (pp. 58-59)

- Express objects as a fraction of a set.

Up until now, the student has dealt with fractions as the fraction of one. Here, the concept of a fraction of a set of more than one is introduced.

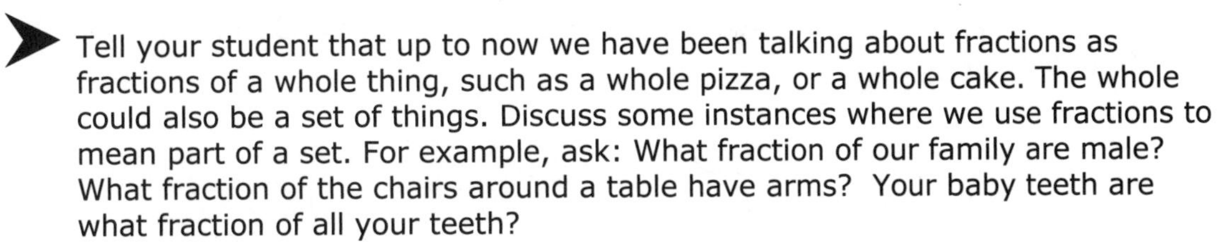

Tell your student that up to now we have been talking about fractions as fractions of a whole thing, such as a whole pizza, or a whole cake. The whole could also be a set of things. Discuss some instances where we use fractions to mean part of a set. For example, ask: What fraction of our family are male? What fraction of the chairs around a table have arms? Your baby teeth are what fraction of all your teeth?

Use **two types of objects**, such as two colors of linking cubes or counters. Set out some of one type and some of the other, such as 4 yellow and 4 red. Ask for the fraction that is yellow. 4 out of 8 are yellow. We can write this as a fraction: $\frac{4}{8}$. This is equivalent to $\frac{1}{2}$. $\frac{1}{2}$ of them are yellow. The 8 objects are divided into two equal groups; one of the two equal groups is yellow.

Use **two-color counters** (such as red and yellow) or coins. Give your student 12 of them. Have him set them out with the same side up (red or heads) and, divide them up into 3 equal groups, and then turn all those in one group over. Ask him what fraction of the total are yellow (or tails). There are 3 parts with the same number of objects. All the objects in one part are yellow. $\frac{1}{3}$ of the total number of objects is yellow. Now have him turn over another of the parts (4 counters) and ask him what fraction are yellow. 2 out of 3 parts, $\frac{2}{3}$ are yellow, or 8 total out of 12 total are yellow, $\frac{8}{12} = \frac{2}{3}$, so $\frac{2}{3}$ are yellow. Repeat with other examples.

Page 58
Learning Task 1, p. 59

1. (a) $\frac{1}{2}$ (b) $\frac{3}{4}$ (c) $\frac{2}{3}$ (d) $\frac{5}{6}$

Workbook Exercise 27

(2) Amount in a Fraction of a Set (p. 59)

- Find the number of objects in a fraction of a set.

Use **two-color counters** or **coins**.

Put out 24 counters and arrange in an array. Ask: How much is one-half of these counters? (12). Your student can show this by turning over half of the counters. Write $\frac{1}{2}$ of 24 = 12. We can also have fractions of a whole where the whole is a set of objects. Have her use the counters to find the following fractions:

$\frac{1}{3}$ of 24 = 8

$\frac{1}{4}$ of 24 = 6

$\frac{1}{6}$ of 24 = 4

$\frac{1}{8}$ of 24 = 3

$\frac{1}{12}$ of 24 = 2

$\frac{1}{6}$ of 24 = 4

She should first divide up the counters into the correct number of equal groups, as in the example. To divide up into equal groups, we can think of the answer to 24 ÷ 6. 24 is divided into 6 equal groups. $\frac{1}{6}$ of 24 is the number of objects in one of those groups.

Now have her find $\frac{2}{6}$ of 24. She should still divide the objects into six equal groups, but now she needs to find the number of objects in two of those groups. Thus

$$\frac{2}{6} \text{ of } 24 = 2 \times (\frac{1}{6} \text{ of } 24) = 2 \times 4 = 8$$

$\frac{2}{6}$ of 24 = 8

Continue with some other examples, such as $\frac{3}{8}$ of 24 = 9 (or 3 x 3), $\frac{5}{12}$ of 24 = 10, etc. Repeat with a different set, such as 15, and find $\frac{1}{3}$ of 15, $\frac{2}{3}$ of 15, $\frac{1}{5}$ of 15, $\frac{3}{5}$ of 15, etc. Emphasize that when the numerator is greater than 1, she can first find the answer when it is 1, and then multiply that answer by the numerator. For example, she should think of $\frac{3}{5}$ of 15 as 3 x ($\frac{1}{5}$ of 15).

Learning Tasks 2-3, p. 59

2. 4
3. 5; 15

Workbook Exercise 28

(3) Multiplication of a Fraction and a Whole Number I (p. 60)

- Multiply a fraction and a whole number where the product is a whole number.

In this section, your student will learn that a fraction *of* a number is the same as the fraction *times* the number. This is sometimes a difficult concept, since up to now multiplication has always *increased* a number. However, multiplication of a fraction less than one by a number *decreases* it. It can help to remember that a fraction *times* a number is the same as a fraction *of* a number so what we are really doing is dividing. $\frac{1}{d} \times n = \frac{n}{d}$. *Times* can sometimes mean *of* even in multiplication of whole numbers. For example, if we are buying 30 oranges in bags of 5, we are buying 6 *of* the 5-orange bags. The unit is a 5-orange bag, and we are buying 6 *of* them. We can also think of $\frac{1}{d} \times n$ as $n \times \frac{1}{d}$. The unit is $\frac{1}{d}$ and we are taking n of them.

Use **two-color counters** or **coins**. Set out 12, and turn over 3 of them.

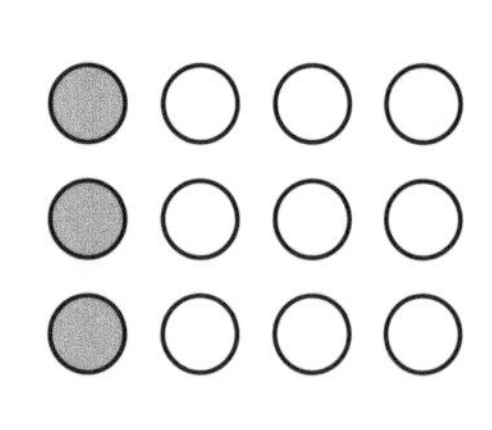

Write $\frac{1}{4}$ of 12. To find the answer, we divide the 12 counters into 4 groups and count the number in one group. We find the equivalent fraction of the improper fraction $\frac{12}{4}$, which is $\frac{3}{1}$ or 3

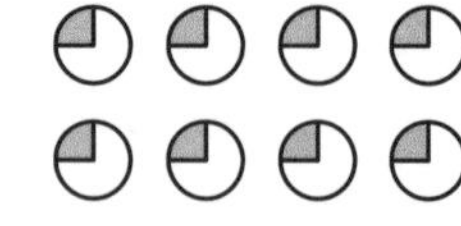

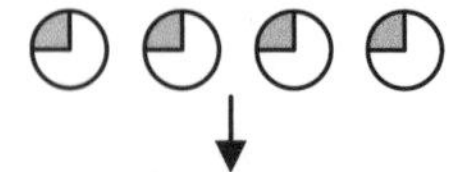

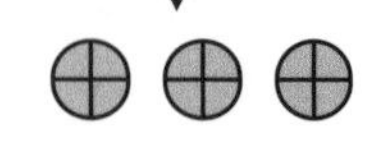

Show that we could also find $\frac{1}{4}$ of each object. We would then have 12 one-fourths, or $12 \times \frac{1}{4}$. If we put the twelve fourths into wholes, we see that $12 \times \frac{1}{4} = 3$. This is the same answer as we got for $\frac{1}{4}$ of 12. So

$$\frac{1}{4} \text{ of } 12 = \frac{1}{4} \times 12 = \frac{1 \times 12}{4} = \frac{12}{4} = 1 \times \frac{12}{4} = 3.$$

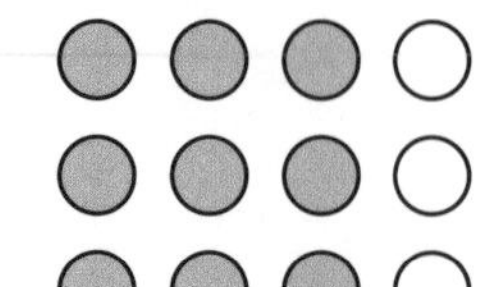

Now, show $\frac{3}{4}$ of 12, first as $3 \times \frac{1}{4} \times 12$

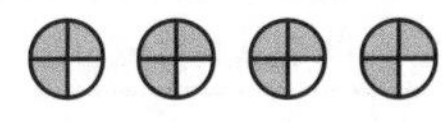
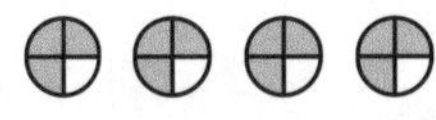

Then, show $\frac{3}{4}$ of each of the 12. We have twelve three-fourths, or 12 x $\frac{3}{4}$. Ask your student how many fourths that is. There are 36 fourths. If they are put into wholes, there are 9 wholes.

$12 \times \frac{3}{4} = \frac{12 \times 3}{4} = \frac{36}{4} = 9$

So, $\frac{3}{4}$ of 12 $= 12 \times \frac{3}{4} = 9$

To solve $\frac{3 \times 12}{4}$, we have shown that this is the same as $3 \times \frac{12}{4} = 3 \times 3 = 9$. Remind your student that to find $\frac{12}{4}$. We divide the numerator and denominator by 4. We can save writing out the steps by showing this in a shortcut crossing out and simplifying (cancellation) way as $\frac{\cancel{12}^{3}}{\cancel{4}_{1}} = 3$. So we can write $\frac{3}{4}$ of $12 = \frac{3 \times \cancel{12}^{3}}{\cancel{4}_{1}} = 9$.

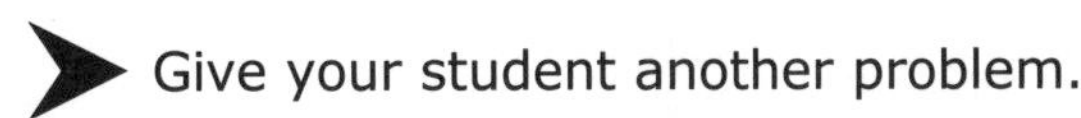

Give your student another problem.

$$\frac{3}{5} \times 40 = \frac{3 \times 40}{5} = 3 \times \frac{40}{5} = 3 \times \frac{\cancel{40}^{8}}{\cancel{5}_{1}} = 3 \times 8 = 24$$

This can be simply written as $\frac{3}{5} \times 40 = \frac{3 \times \cancel{40}^{8}}{\cancel{5}_{1}} = 24$

or even more simply as $\frac{3}{\cancel{5}_{1}} \times \cancel{40}^{8} = 24$

Top of p. 60, Learning Task 4, p. 60

5; 15

4. 15

Further practice is given in Mental Math 17.

Workbook Exercise 29

(4) Multiplication of a Fraction and a Whole Number II (p. 60)

- Multiply a fraction and a whole number where the product is not a whole number.

Draw 8 circles and discuss with your student how to find $\frac{1}{4}$ of 10. He can put 8 of them into 4 equal groups, but two are left over. He needs to divide each of these into half and put one half into each group.

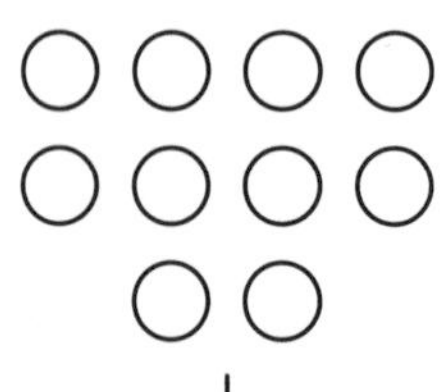

$\frac{1}{4}$ of 10 = $\frac{1}{4} \times 10 = 2\frac{1}{2}$.

Point out that this is the same as $\frac{10}{4}$ converted into the mixed number, $2\frac{1}{2}$. Thus

$\frac{1}{4}$ of 10 = $1 \times \frac{10}{4} = 2\frac{1}{2}$

Now have him find $\frac{3}{4}$ of 10. Since $\frac{1}{4} \times 10 = 2\frac{1}{2}$, then $\frac{3}{4} \times 10 = 3 \times 2\frac{1}{2}$.

We can find $3 \times 2\frac{1}{2}$ by finding 3×2 and $3 \times \frac{1}{2}$.

$$3 \times 2 = 6 \qquad 3 \times \frac{1}{2} = \frac{3}{2} = 1\frac{1}{2}$$

$$3 \times 2\frac{1}{2} = 6 + 1\frac{1}{2} = 7\frac{1}{2}$$

It is important that your student understands the procedures given here so that he understands concretely what is going on when we find the fraction of a whole number. **After** your student has done the exercise, you may wish to explain a short-cut method for doing these kinds of problems:

Since $\frac{1}{4} \times 10 = \frac{10}{4} = \frac{5}{2}$, then $\frac{3}{4} \times 10 = 3 \times \frac{5}{2}$:

$$3 \times \frac{5}{2} = \frac{3 \times 5}{2} = \frac{15}{2} = 7\frac{1}{2}$$

Using the cancellation method, we can cut out some steps:

$$\frac{3}{4} \times 10 = \frac{3 \times \cancel{10}^{5}}{\cancel{4}_{2}} = \frac{15}{2} = 7\frac{1}{2}$$

Learning Tasks 5-6, p. 60

Draw pictures to illustrate solution.

5. $6\frac{3}{4}$

6. (a) $\frac{1}{2}$ of 12 = $\frac{12}{2}$ = **6** (b) $\frac{1}{5}$ of 20 = $\frac{20}{5}$ = **4**

   (c) $\frac{1}{6}$ of 4 = $\frac{4}{6}$ = $\mathbf{\frac{2}{3}}$ (d) $\frac{2}{3}$ of 9 = 2 x $\frac{9}{3}$ = 2 x 3 = **6**

   (e) $\frac{3}{8}$ of 16 = 3 x $\frac{16}{8}$ = 3 x 2 = **6**

   (f) $\frac{2}{3}$ of 10 = 2 x $\frac{10}{3}$ = 2 x $3\frac{1}{3}$ = $\mathbf{6\frac{2}{3}}$

Further practice in multiplying a whole number by a mixed number is given in Mental Math 18.

Workbook Exercise 30

(5) Word Problems I (p. 61)

- Relate fractions of a whole to units in a part-whole diagram.

In *Primary Mathematics 3*, students learned to model word problems involving multiplication and division where a part-whole bar was divided up into equal units. These models are described on p. 24 of this guide. Here, the student will associate a unit with a fraction of a bar in order to solve word problems involving fractions. This was introduced on p. 39 of the guide, where the bar represented one whole. Here, the bar represents the total amount, and each unit is a fraction of the total.

In the workbook exercise 31, require your student to draw models for problems 3 and 4. These problems are easy enough to solve without modeling, but the problems in exercise 33 will be more easily solved with modeling, so it is worthwhile learning this method here.

Tell your student that we can draw fraction bars where the total length of the bar is a total greater than one, rather than one whole. For example, with $\frac{2}{3}$ of 18, we can draw a bar to stand for 18. How many parts should it have? (3). Divide it up into three equal parts. We can call each part a unit. We have 3 units. What is the value of each unit? (6) This is the same as $\frac{1}{3}$ of 18. How many units would be the same as $\frac{2}{3}$? (2)

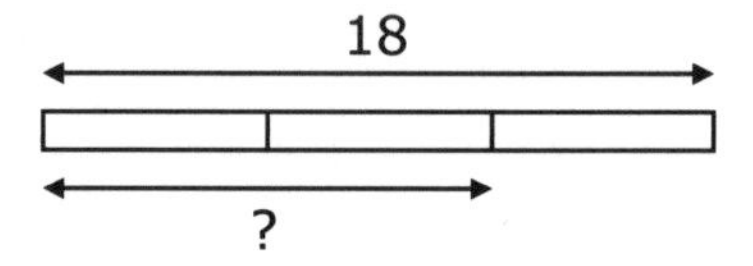

$\frac{3}{3}$ = 3 units = 18

$\frac{1}{3}$ = 1 unit = 18 ÷ 3 = 6

$\frac{2}{3}$ = 2 units = 6 x 2 = 12

What is the value of 2 units? (12). So $\frac{2}{3}$ of 18 is 12. When we diagram fraction problems, the first step is usually to find the value of one unit.

Learning Task 7, p. 61

In the first method, point out that we are first finding the value of one unit.

7. 1: 8; 16; 16
   2: 16; 16

Workbook Exercise 31

(6) Fraction of a Whole (pp. 61-62)

- Express a part as a fraction of a whole.

In the first section of this part, the student learned how to find a fraction of a set. The set is a whole. So 2 parts out of 6 can be expressed as $\frac{1}{3}$. 2 is $\frac{1}{3}$ of 6. This concept is extended here to situations where the part is a different unit of measurement than the whole. For example, 30 minutes is $\frac{1}{2}$ of 1 hour. In order to find what fraction the part is of the whole, both the part and the whole have to be in the same units.

Use some **coins** and **a dollar bill**. Set out 5 pennies and 15 dimes. Ask, "What fraction of the total coins are the pennies?" It is 5 pennies out of 20 coins, or $\frac{5}{20} = \frac{1}{4}$. Remind him we use the simplest form. 5 pennies is $\frac{1}{4}$ of 20 coins. To find the fraction, we put the amount in one part (5) in the numerator, and the **total** amount in the denominator. Ask, "What fraction of the total coins are dimes?" It is $\frac{15}{20} = \frac{3}{4}$.

Set out 25 pennies. Move one aside. Ask your student, "One penny is what fraction of 25 pennies?" It is $\frac{1}{25}$. The penny is the part, 25 is the total. Move 5 pennies aside and ask, "Five pennies is what fraction of 25 pennies?" Replace the pennies with a quarter. Ask, "What fraction of a quarter is 5¢?" It is also $\frac{1}{5}$. Point out that to find the answer, we thought of the quarter as 25¢. To find out what fraction something is of another, we need to have both things in the same measurement value or unit. The unit here is a cent. Ask him what the unit was before, when we had the 5 pennies and 10 dimes. It was the number of coins. The pennies were **coins**, and so were the dimes, and the total number of coins was 20. Now, we are finding the fraction of total cents, so we need to think of the quarter as 25 cents. Show a dollar bill and ask, "What fraction is one dime of a dollar?" We have to change both into cents and find the number of cents in a dime out of the number of cents in a dollar. A dime is 10¢ and a dollar is 100¢, so a dime is $\frac{10}{100} = \frac{1}{10}$ of a dollar. Or we can change the dollar into 10 dimes. One dime is $\frac{1}{10}$ of ten dimes.

Discuss the following or similar problems:

- 4 inches is what fraction of 1 foot?
  To find this, we change the foot into inches. 1 foot = 12 inches. Now we find 4 inches out of 12 inches. $\frac{4}{12} = \frac{1}{3}$. 4 inches is $\frac{1}{3}$ of 1 foot.
- 6 cups is what fraction of a gallon?
  We convert the larger measurement into the smaller. 1 gallon is 16 cups. $\frac{6}{16} = \frac{3}{8}$. 6 cups is $\frac{3}{8}$ of a gallon.
- What fraction of $1\frac{1}{2}$ m is 50 cm? We change $1\frac{1}{2}$ m into 150 cm. $\frac{50}{150} = \frac{1}{3}$. 50 cm is $\frac{1}{3}$ of $1\frac{1}{2}$ m.

Learning Tasks 8-10, pp. 61-62

8. $\frac{3}{4}$ 9. $\frac{1}{7}$ 10. $\frac{4}{25}$

Workbook Exercise 32

Note: Problem 2.(b) of Exercise 32 in the 3rd edition and the first US edition of Primary Mathematics is inappropriate unless your student has already learned to measure angles and that a right angle is 90°. You may want to replace it with: "What fraction of $1\frac{1}{2}$ hours is 50 minutes?"

(7) Word Problems II (p. 62)

- Determine the whole from the value of a fractional part of the whole.

In earlier word problems, the student was given a whole and asked to find the fractional part by division. Here, the student will be given a fractional part and then asked to find the whole. This can be visualized using a bar model where each fraction is a unit. If the fractional part is a unit fraction, the whole can be found by multiplication.

For example, if 20 is $\frac{1}{4}$ of the whole, then the whole is 20 x 4.

If the fractional part has a numerator other than 1, we first find the value of the unit fraction before finding the value of the whole. For example, if 60 is $\frac{3}{4}$ of the whole, then we first find $\frac{1}{4}$ of the whole by dividing 60 by 3 to get 20, and then multiplying 20 by 4 to get the whole.

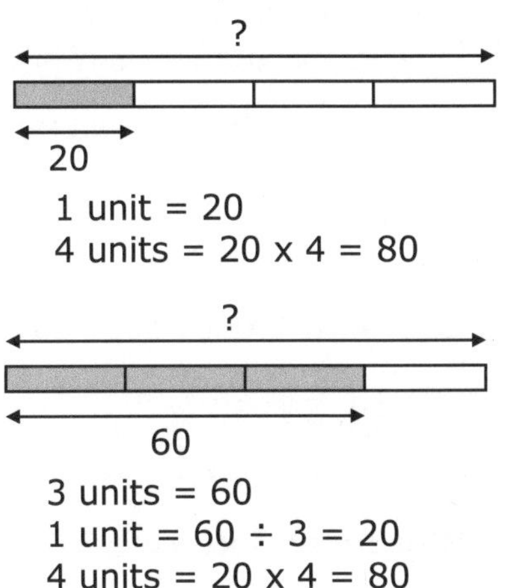

This is a concrete introduction to division of a fraction, which will be taught in *Primary Mathematics 6B*.

Use small objects such as unit cubes. Put 15 of them in 5 groups of 3. Cover up 2 groups each with an index card.

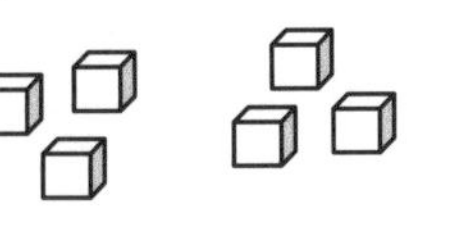

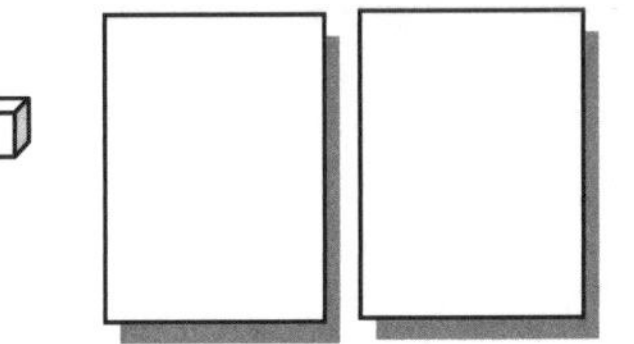

Tell your student that $\frac{3}{5}$ of the blocks are uncovered and ask how many total blocks there are. (15). Tell her that this is easy to find because we know how many blocks are in each group. So if we are just told that 9 is $\frac{3}{5}$ of the total, we need to find how many blocks are in each group. Show how we can diagram this, and then divide the 9 by 3 to find how many are in each group. We can call each group a unit, since the value, or the amount in each group, is the same.

?

9

3 units = 9
1 unit = 9 ÷ 3 = 3
5 units = 3 x 5 = 15

 Discuss and help your student diagram the following problem:

- I spent $\frac{3}{7}$ of my money on some clothes. The clothes cost \$45. How much money did I start with? How much money do I have left?

$\frac{3}{7}$ of the bar represents \$45.

$\frac{1}{7}$ of the bar represents \$15.

The whole bar represents \$105.
The amount left is represented by $\frac{4}{7}$ of the bar, or can be calculated by subtracting the total amount from the amount spent.

\$45

3 units = \$45
1 unit = \$45 ÷ 3 = \$15
7 units = \$15 x 7 = \$105
4 units = \$15 x 4 = \$60

 **Learning Task 11, p. 62**

11. 10; 50; 50

 **Workbook Exercise 33**

(8) Two-Step Word Problems (pp. 63-64)

- Solve up to two-step word problems which involve fractions of a set.

Learning Tasks 12-14

The examples in the text show different methods for solving the word problems. Discuss the different methods with your student. He may use any method of preference in solving the problems in the workbook exercises. Encourage him to model the problem if he has difficulty.

12. 1: 12; 12 2: 12; 12 3: 4; 12; 12

13. 6; 30; 30

14. 1: $\frac{3}{8}$; $\frac{3}{8}$ 2: $\frac{3}{8}$; $\frac{3}{8}$

Discuss the following problem:

- A jar contains some beads. $\frac{1}{5}$ of the beads are red, $\frac{3}{10}$ of the beads are white, and the rest are blue. If 15 of the beads are white, how many total beads are there? How many are blue?

We need to divide the bar up into equal units, so we use the equivalent fraction $\frac{2}{10}$ for the fraction of beads that are red. Divide the bar into 10 units. The red beads are represented by 2 units, and the white beads by 3 units.

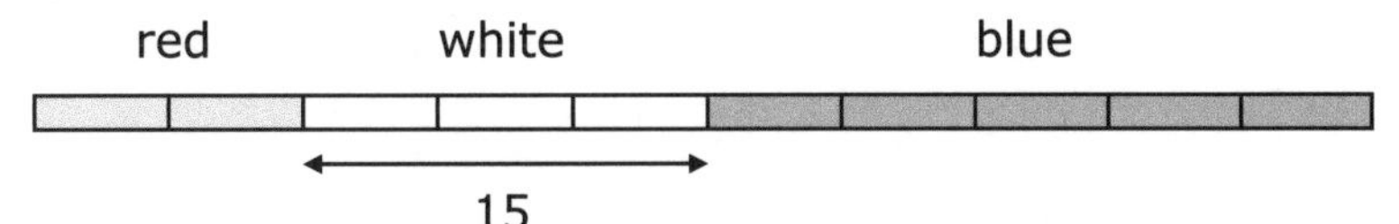

There are 5 units left, so those represent the blue beads.

3 units = 15	or	$\frac{3}{10}$ of the total = 15
1 unit = 15 ÷ 3 = 5		$\frac{1}{10}$ of the total = 5
10 units = 5 x 10 = 50		$\frac{10}{10}$ of the total (all) = 50
5 units = 5 x 5 = 25		$\frac{5}{10}$ of the total ($\frac{1}{2}$ of the total) = 25

There are a total of 50 beads. 25 of them are blue.

Workbook Exercises 34-35

(9) Practice (p. 65)

➢ Practice problems involving fractions.

Practice 3C, p. 65

1. (a) 6 (b) 24 (c) $\frac{2}{3}$ (d) $8\frac{1}{3}$

2. (a) 9 (b) 6 (c) $\frac{3}{4}$ (d) $7\frac{1}{2}$

3. Length of bookshelf = $\frac{3}{4}$ x 3 m = $\mathbf{2\frac{1}{4}}$ **m**

4. Total amount of time = 5 x $\frac{3}{4}$ hour = $\frac{15}{4}$ hour = $\mathbf{3\frac{3}{4}}$ **hours**

5. (a) Fraction that do not wear glasses = 1 - $\frac{2}{5}$ = $\mathbf{\frac{3}{5}}$

   (b) 2 units = 16
   1 unit = 16 ÷ 2 = 8
   Total students = 5 units = 8 x 5 = **40**

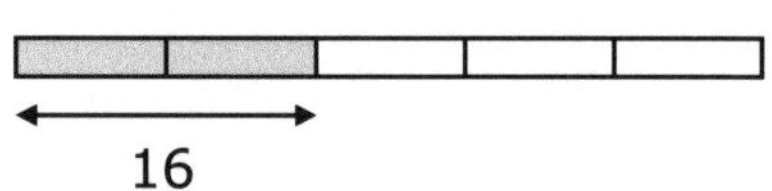

6. Number of eggs left = $\frac{1}{3}$ x 30 = **10**

7. $\frac{1}{3}$ of the total cards = 8. Total cards = 8 x 3 = **24**

8. $\frac{1}{4}$ of the total money = \$6. Total money = \$6 x 4 = **\$24**

Review

Review B, pp. 66-69

1. (a) 7003 (b) 15,212
2. (a) four thousand, six hundred sixty
   (b) thirty-five thousand, six hundred
   (c) forty-seven thousand, nineteen
   (d) fifty-two thousand, four hundred seventy-three
3. (a) 47,355; 74,355; 74,535; 75,435
   (b) 23,232; 23,322; 32,223; 33,222
4. (a) 16,060 (b) 69,516
5. 10,000
6. (a) 410 (b) 690 (c) 5970
7. (a) 700 (b) 5600 (c) 7400
8. (a) 4590 (b) 456 r2
9. (a) 9 (b) 8
   (c) 3 (d) 2
10. (a) 1 or 3
    (b) 18, 36, 54, 72, 90, ...
11. (a) $\frac{3}{4}$ (b) $\frac{7}{9}$
    (c) $\frac{11}{12}$ (d) $\frac{1}{5}$
    (e) $\frac{1}{4}$ (f) $\frac{1}{8}$
12. (a) $\frac{5}{8}$ (b) $\frac{1}{3}$ (c) $\frac{1}{6}$
    (d) $\frac{1}{2}$ (e) $\frac{3}{4}$ (f) $\frac{1}{2}$
13. (a) $\frac{4}{9}$ (b) $\frac{2}{3}$
14. $\frac{1}{12}, \frac{1}{3}, \frac{3}{5}, \frac{4}{4}, \frac{3}{2}$
15. (a) 6 (b) 18
    (c) 2 (d) 3
16. (a) $\frac{4}{5}$ (b) $\frac{1}{6}$ (c) $1\frac{1}{3}$ (d) $2\frac{1}{4}$

17. (a) $3\frac{1}{3}$ (b) 3 (c) $4\frac{1}{2}$ (d) $3\frac{2}{7}$

18. (a) $\frac{11}{7}$ (b) $\frac{14}{5}$ (c) $\frac{25}{8}$ (d) $\frac{29}{10}$

19. Total pizza eaten = $10 \times \frac{1}{4}$ = $\mathbf{2\frac{1}{2}}$

20. $\frac{3}{10}$ of the oil = 150 g

$\frac{1}{10}$ of the oil = 150 g ÷ 3 = 50 g

all of the oil = 50 g x 10 = **500 g**

21. 5 units = 20 ℓ
1 unit = 20 ℓ ÷ 5 = 4 ℓ
Capacity = 6 units = 4 ℓ x 6 = **24 ℓ**

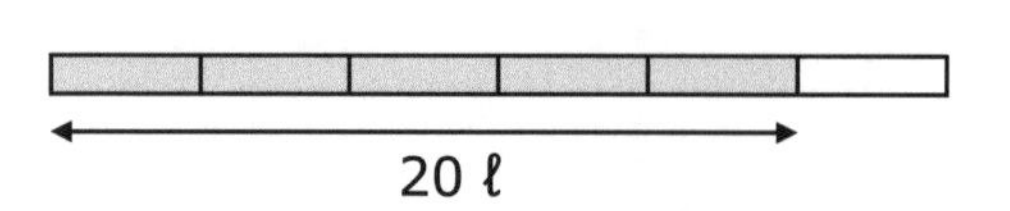

22. Fraction left = $\frac{1}{4}$

Amount left = $\frac{1}{4}$ x 100 = **25**

23. Given price = \$18 + \$24 + \$36 = \$78

Amount spent = $\frac{1}{2}$ x \$78 = **\$39**

(Or find half of cost of each item and then add.)

24. (a) Fraction that were boys = $1 - \frac{4}{5} = \mathbf{\frac{1}{5}}$

(b) 1 unit = 8
Total number of children
= 5 units = 8 x 5 = **40**

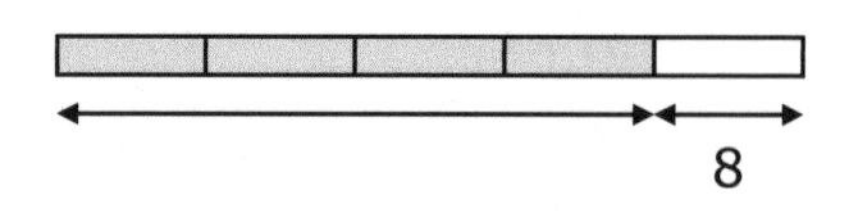

(c) Difference in number of girls and boys = 3 units = 8 x 3 = **24**

Workbook Review 3

Unit 4 Tables and Graphs

Part 1 Presenting Data

(1) Tables and Bar Graphs (pp. 70-71)

- Read and interpret data presented in a table.
- Construct a bar graph from data given in a table.

In *Primary Mathematics 3*, students learned to read and interpret bar graphs, but were not required to construct them. In this unit they will learn to present data in a table and construct bar graphs using data from a table. At this level, the students should be provided with the horizontal and vertical axes when they are asked to construct graphs.

Pages 70-71

Discuss the relationship between the information on the cards, in the table, and the bar graph. Discuss the information given. Who weighs the most? Who weighs the least? How much more does one child weigh than another?

Learning Task 1, p. 71

US›1. (a) Pablo (b) 6
3d›1. (a) Hassan (b) 6

(c) Help your student set up a bar graph on graph paper. Draw the axes for your student. Ask how high the values should go on the vertical axis? They should go to some number slightly beyond the highest number, such as 15 or 20. Count the divisions on the graph paper and help your student decide how much each should represent. For example, if you are using the centimeter graph paper in the appendix, each centimeter could stand for one book if your student wants to make the graph take most of the page. If he wanted the graph to take half the page, each division could stand for 2 books. The vertical axis should be labeled.

Find some tables and bar graphs from other sources, such as texts or the newspaper. Discuss the advantages to bar graphs versus tables. Bar graphs make it easier to visualize the relationship between the data, such as which item is the greatest, but it is easier to find information about actual amounts from a table.

Workbook Exercises 36-37

(2) Bar Graphs (p. 72)

- Construct a table from data given in a bar graph.
- Solve problems using data presented in a bar graph.

Learning Tasks 2-3, p. 72

2. (a) 15 (b) Feb., Jun. (c) Jan. (d) 6 (e) Feb.

3. Guide your student in designing a table.

Continue to discuss the relative value of bar graphs versus tables. Which types of questions in learning task 2 would be easier to answer with a bar graph and which would be easier to answer with a table?

You may want to teach your student how to enter data and create graphs using spreadsheet software. Enter data from one of the learning tasks or exercises and investigate the kinds of graphs that can be generated from the data. Discuss effective ways of presenting data, including the color of the graphs.

Workbook Exercise 38

(3) Tables (p. 73)

➢ Solve problems using data presented in tables.

Learning Tasks 4-5, p 73

4. (a) 27 (b) 6 (c) 24

5. (a) 5; 13; 14; 29
   (b) 13 (c) 29

Help your student construct a double bar graph of the data in learning task 4, or show him the graph below. Discuss the information that is evident from this kind of a graph, such as the fact that both cooking and dancing were more popular with women than men, but that the difference in popularity between women and men was greater for cooking.

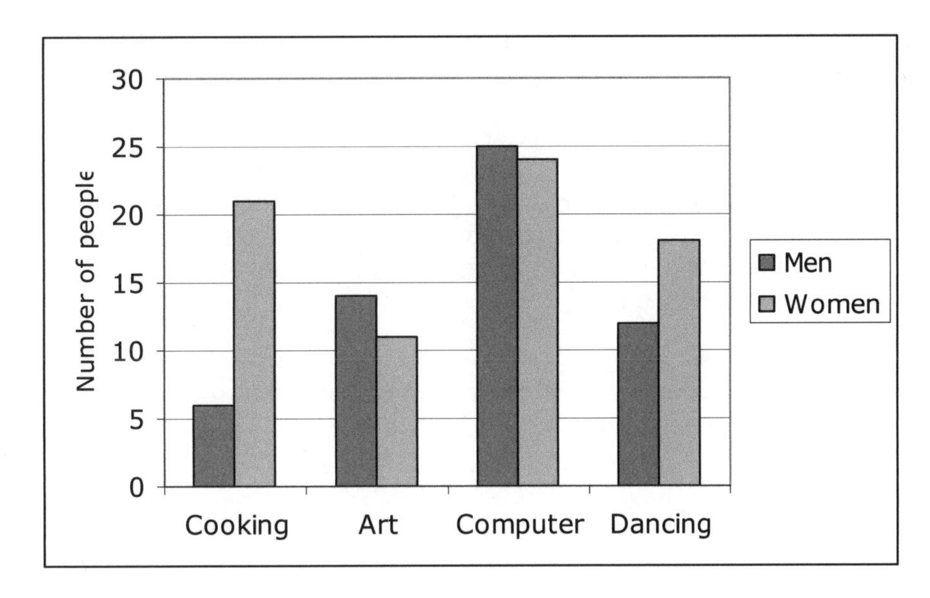

Workbook Exercises 39-40

(4) Collecting and Presenting Data

➤ Collect data and present it in a table and a bar graph.

With your student, decide on some kind of data to collect that is relevant to his experience. Before collecting the data, try to formulate a hypothesis, or something he could find out from the data. One option would be to take a paragraph and count the number of times each vowel appears. A hypothesis could be that *e* is the most frequently used vowel.

Teach him how to tally the information by creating a chart and writing a mark for each item. Every fifth mark crosses the previous four. That way he can count his results by counting by tens and fives.

Have him create a table and a bar graph from the data.
Help him determine the size and divisions for the vertical axis.

Discuss the data. For example, which vowel was used the most? Have him write some conclusions about his data.

Look for other opportunities to collect and display data. He may want to use computer software to do the graphing and look at the various ways the data can be presented other than a bar graph. However, he should do some graphing without the computer in order to gain experience in determining how long to draw the vertical axis and what scale to use for it, and how to make his graph appealing and easy to read.

Unit 5 Angles

Part 1 Measuring Angles

(1) Measuring Angles (pp. 74-75)

- Understand the use of degrees for measuring angles.
- Recognize right angles as 90°.
- Measure angles less than 180° with a protractor.

In *Primary Mathematics 3B*, students learned to recognize angles and classify them as right angles, greater than right angles, or less than right angles. Here, the student will learn to measure angles.

The degree is derived from the Babylonian base 60 system. They may have assigned 360 degrees to a circle because they found that it took about 360 days for the sun to complete one year's circuit across the sky. 360 is conveniently divisible by 2, 3, 4, 5, 6, 8, 9, 10, 12, 15, 18, and 20, so the degree is a nice unit to divide the circle into an equal number of parts. 180 degrees is $\frac{1}{2}$ of a circle, 120 degrees is $\frac{1}{3}$ of a circle, 90 degrees is $\frac{1}{4}$ of a circle, and so on.

Use two strips of card board joined at one end with a brad. Open it and draw several angles along the inside edges at different amounts of turning. Remind your student that the size of an angle is related to the amount of turning of one strip relative to the other. The size of the arms on an angle is not important; an angle with short arms needs just as much turning of one strip relative to the other as an angle with longer arms.

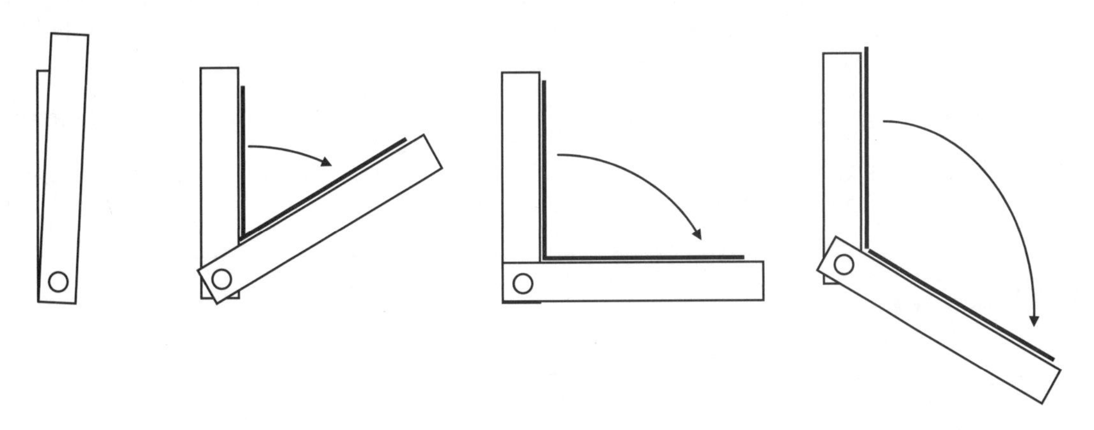

Tell your student that the amount of turning in an angle is measured in **degrees**. One degree is a turn of $\frac{1}{360}$ of the way around a circle. Show your student a **protractor**. A turn of a full circle is 360 degrees. We can measure degrees with a protractor.

Draw some angles and demonstrate the use of a protractor. The vertex (point) of the angle must be placed at the center of the base line and one arm lined up along the base line. In some protractors the base line is along the bottom edge, but in others is in a line a short way up from the bottom edge. Show her that there are two scales, one which starts at 0 on the left side of the protractor and one that starts at 0 on the right side.

Discuss abbreviations and naming conventions for degrees and angles. *Degrees* is abbreviated with a little circle superscript. Show her how we write degrees, such as 90°. The term *angle* is abbreviated ∠. Angles are sometimes labeled with lowercase letters. Points are labeled with uppercase letters. A drawing showing an angle can be labeled with three points, one on each arm and one at the vertex, or point. The angle is named by the three points, with the vertex in the middle, and using the symbol for angle.

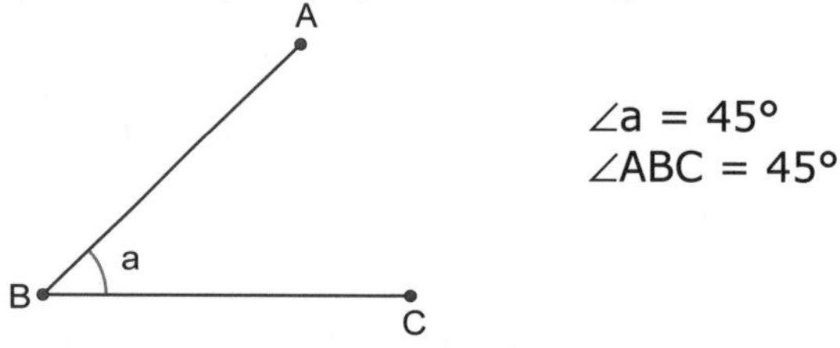

Ask your student to measure the right angle corner of a piece of paper. How many degrees is a right angle? Draw a variety of angles less than 180° and let your student practice measuring them. Point out that if the arms are too short, she can extend the arms using the edge of the protractor as a straight-edge.

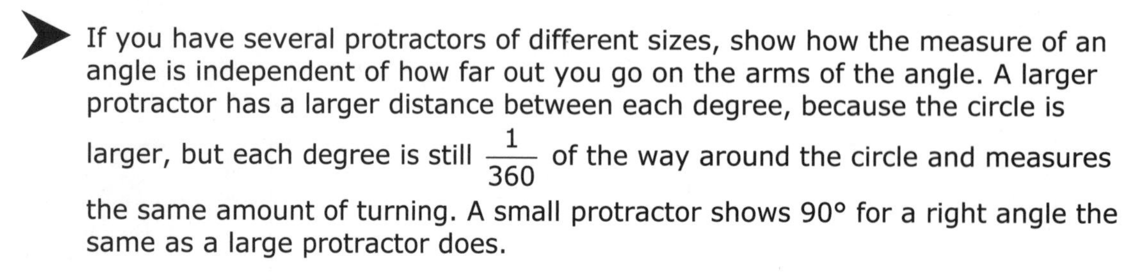

If you have several protractors of different sizes, show how the measure of an angle is independent of how far out you go on the arms of the angle. A larger protractor has a larger distance between each degree, because the circle is larger, but each degree is still $\frac{1}{360}$ of the way around the circle and measures the same amount of turning. A small protractor shows 90° for a right angle the same as a large protractor does.

Page 74
Learning Task 1, p. 75

1. 20; 140

Workbook Exercise 41

(2) Constructing Angles (p. 75)

- Estimate the measure of angles less than 180°.
- Draw angles of a given measurement less than 180°.

Draw some angles and have your student estimate the measure of the angles before actually measuring it.

Challenge him to draw some angles of a certain number of degrees and then to see how close he came by measurement.

Learning Task 2, p. 75

2. 75; 120

Learning Task 3, p. 75

Show your student how to draw angles. To draw angles, first draw a line and mark a point on it, which can be at one end, where the vertex or point of the angle will be. Put the center point of the protractor on that point and line up the base line of the protractor directly on the top of the drawn line. Mark a point on the curved edge of the protractor corresponding to the required degrees. Remove the protractor, and then use the straight edge to connect the vertex with the marked point. Have your student draw a right angle and several angles larger or smaller than a right angle.

Workbook Exercise 42

(3) Angles Greater than 180° (pp. 76-77)

- Measure angles greater than 180°.
- Estimate the measure of angles greater than 180°.
- Draw angles of a given measurement greater than 180°.

Learning Task 4, p. 76

Use the cardboard strips joined at one end to illustrate this activity. Tell your student that when turning all the way around a circle there are 360°. What would be the number of degrees going $\frac{1}{4}$ of the way around? ($\frac{1}{4}$ of 360° = 90°, a right angle.) For going $\frac{1}{2}$ of the way around? ($\frac{1}{2}$ of 360° = 180°, a straight line.) For going $\frac{3}{4}$ of the way around? ($\frac{3}{4}$ of 360° = 3 x 90° = 270°.) An angle can be larger than 180°.

Learning Task 5, p. 76

Show your student how to measure angles greater than 180°, as shown in learning task 5. There are two methods.

One is to imagine a straight line out from one of the arms, and to measure the angle formed in the other direction with the second arm. In the picture in the text, if you follow the turning in a counter-clockwise direction, half way around is 180°, and the rest of the way around is 60°, as read on the inside scale. Thus the measure of the angle is 180° + 60° = 240°.

The other method is to imagine a circle cut into two parts by the two arms, with the vertex at the center. There are two angles, a smaller one less than 180° and a larger one greater than 180°. Measure the smaller one, which in the picture in the text is 120°. The measure of the larger angle is the degrees for the entire circle minus the degrees for the smaller angle, or 360° - 120° = 240°.

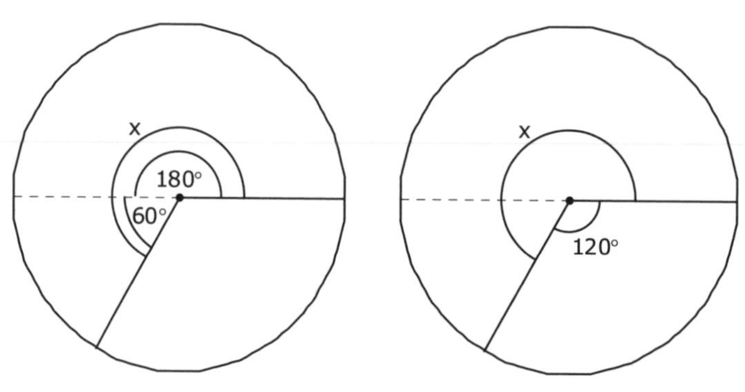

Learning Tasks 6-7, pp. 77

Trace the angles in learning task 7 on another piece of paper so that your student can extend the arms.

6. 320
7. $\angle g = 240°$; $\angle h = 230°$; $\angle k = 300°$

Draw other angles greater than 180° for your student to measure. Ask her to estimate the size of the angle first.

Learning Task 8, p. 77

Show your student how to construct an angle greater than 180°. She must determine the smaller angle that would be formed by subtracting from 360° and construct it using a protractor. The opposite angle is the angle needed.

Ask your student to construct other angles greater than 180°.

Workbook Exercise 43

(4) Finding Unknown Angles (p. 77)

- Find complementary angles

If certain properties of geometric figures are known, some angles can be found without direct measurement. The student is introduced to this concept here with rectangles. A rectangle has four right angles. If one of the corners is divided into two angles, and the measure of one of the angles given, the other angle can be found by subtraction. The two angles that form a right angle are called complementary angles. (Two angles that form a straight line are called supplementary angles.) The student does not need to learn the term *complementary* at this point.

Constructions in the text and workbook where unknown angles must be found by computation rather than direct measure are not drawn to scale. The student cannot check his answer by measuring.

➤ Use the rectangles in the appendix or draw your own large enough so that the corners can be measured using a protractor. Ask your student for the measure of each corner of a rectangle. Draw a line from one corner to the opposite corner and ask your student to find the measure of each of the smaller angles.

$\angle CBD = 30°$, $\angle ABD = 60°$; $\angle GFH = 53°$, $\angle EFH = 37°$; $\angle KJL = 74°$, $\angle IJL = 16°$

Ask him to add the two angles together. Their sum will always be 90°. Note that we label the corners of the rectangle and name the rectangle by the labeled corners. Thus the first rectangle can be called rectangle ABCD. The angles are named from the names of the corner points, with the vertex for the angle the middle of the three letters.

Discuss how we can find one of the angles without measuring if we know the measure of the other angle. If we know one angle, we can find the other by subtracting the known angle from the total right angle, 90°.

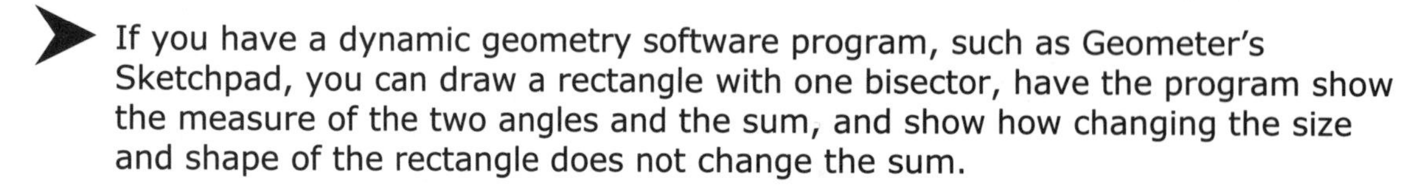

➤ If you have a dynamic geometry software program, such as Geometer's Sketchpad, you can draw a rectangle with one bisector, have the program show the measure of the two angles and the sum, and show how changing the size and shape of the rectangle does not change the sum.

Learning Task 9, p. 77

8. $\angle BAC = 64°$

Workbook Exercise 44

Unit 6 Perpendicular and Parallel Lines

Part 1 Perpendicular Lines

(1) Identifying Perpendicular Lines (pp. 78-79)

- Identify perpendicular lines.

Page 78-79

Perpendicular lines are lines that meet at a right angle. They are marked by a little square.

Show your student a **set-square** (triangle). Let her measure the angles on the set-square with a **protractor**. Draw some intersecting lines and show her how she can use the 90° angle of the set-square to determine whether they are perpendicular lines.

Note that lines are named by the names of two points labeled with capital letters on the line (even if the two points are not drawn as little filled circles).

A line theoretically goes on indefinitely in either direction. You may wish to introduce the term *line segment*, which is the segment of the line between two points.

Learning Task 1, p. 79

1. (a) $CD \perp BC$; $AD \perp AB$
   (b) $EI \perp HI$; $EF \perp EI$; $GH \perp FG$

Workbook Exercise 45

(2) Constructing Perpendicular Lines (p. 80)

➢ Construct perpendicular lines.

Learning Task 2, p. 80

Show your student how to construct a line perpendicular to a given line through a given point using a **set-square**. Line up one side of the set-square with the line, slide it along until the perpendicular side of the set-square touches the point, and then draw a line from the given line through the point along the side of the set-square.

Draw some lines and points and have your student construct a perpendicular line through the point.

Learning Task 3, p. 80

Examine the lines in the text and discuss ways to determine whether they are perpendicular. One way is to draw a rectangle around each line from where the line intersects corners of the grid such that the line goes from one corner of the rectangle to the other and compare the rectangles. If they are the same dimensions, but at right angles to each other, then the lines are perpendicular. Or, count the steps from where one line intersects a corner to where it intersects another corner. One line goes over and down the same amount as the other line goes up and over. For example, in this drawing one line goes to the right 5 squares and down 2 squares from one grid corner to the next, and the other goes up 5 squares and to the right 2 squares.

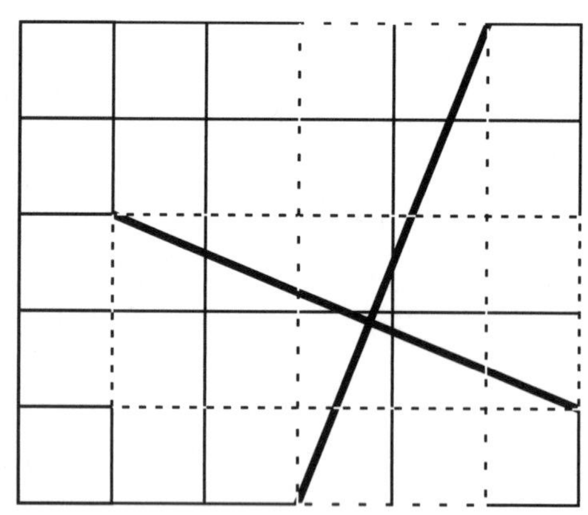

Give your student some **square grid paper** (you can copy the centimeter paper in the appendix) and have her draw some perpendicular lines and then check them with the **set-square**.

Workbook Exercise 46

Part 2 Parallel Lines

(1) Identifying Parallel Lines (pp. 81-82)

- Identify parallel lines.

Pages 81-82

Parallel lines are two straight lines drawn on a plane such that they will never intersect even if they are extended indefinitely in both directions.

Introduce the terms **horizontal lines** and **vertical lines**. Horizontal lines are parallel to the horizon. Vertical lines are perpendicular to horizontal lines. Generally, lines drawn on paper are considered to be horizontal if they are drawn parallel to the top or bottom of the paper, whereas lines drawn parallel to the sides of the paper are considered to be vertical lines, irrespective of the actual horizon.

Learning Task 1, p. 82

1. ST ⊥ RS
   PT // QR

Workbook Exercise 47

(2) Constructing Parallel Lines (p. 83)

- Construct parallel lines.

Learning Task 2, p. 83

Show your student how to construct a line parallel to a given line through a given point using a **set-square** and a **ruler**. Line up one side of right angle of the set-square with the line, line up the ruler with the other side, slide the set-square along the ruler until the first side intersects with the point, and then draw a line along the first side. Have your student practice drawing lines parallel to a given line through a point. Add another point on the new line and have your student construct a rectangle with the two points as two of the corners.

Learning Task 3, p. 83

Give your student some square grid paper and have her draw parallel lines. She can draw patterns made up of parallel and perpendicular lines.

Workbook Exercise 48

Unit 7 Area and Perimeter

Part 1 Rectangles and Squares

(1) Area and Perimeter (pp. 84-86)

- Find one dimension of a rectangle given its perimeter and the other dimension.
- Find the area of a square given its perimeter and one dimension.
- Find one dimension of a rectangle given its area and the other dimension.

In *Primary Mathematics 3*, students learned to find the area and perimeter of a rectangle given its length and width. This is reviewed here and extended to finding one dimension given the other dimension and either the area or perimeter. Students will be asked to find a side of a square given its area. They should be able to recognize square numbers, but the term or symbol for square root is not used here.

Page 84

Review finding the area and perimeter of rectangles. Discuss different methods of finding the perimeter:

Method 1 Add the sides: 9 cm + 5 cm + 9 cm + 5 cm = **28 cm**

Method 2 Add the length and width: 9 cm + 5 cm = 14 cm
Double the total length: 14 cm x 2 = 28 cm

Method 3 Double the length: 9 cm x 2 = 18 cm
Double the width: 5 cm x 2 = 10 cm
Add the two products: 18 cm + 10 cm = 28 cm

Provide some other examples using **centimeter graph paper**. Draw some squares as well. Note that the perimeter of a square can be found by multiplying the length of one side by 4.

By way of review of fractions, have your student find the perimeter of some squares with fractional length. For example, have him find the perimeter of a square of side $3\frac{1}{4}$ cm, or the area of a rectangle with width 3 cm and length $4\frac{1}{2}$ cm. Do not do areas of rectangles where both dimensions are fractions.

Learning Task 1, p. 85

Discuss different methods of finding one dimension given the perimeter and the other dimension.

Method 1 Divide the perimeter into two: 24 m ÷ 2 = 12 m
Subtract the length: 12 m − 8 m = **4 m**

Dividing the perimeter in two gives the total for one width and length. If this is difficult for your student to conceive, tell him to pretend the rectangle is cut at one corner and the edges are straightened out. Draw a part-whole model to show this:

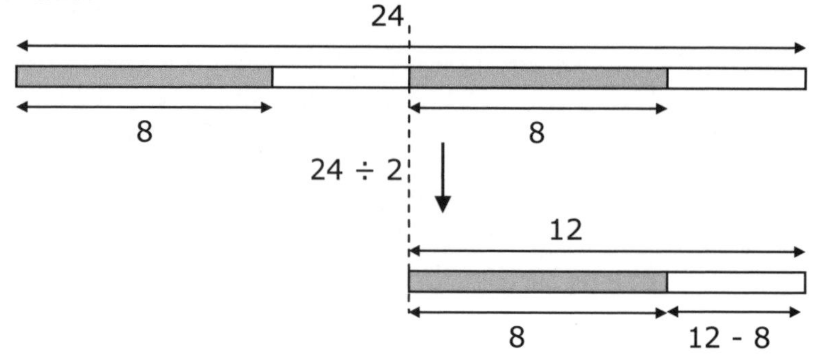

Method 2 Subtract the length twice from the perimeter:
24 m − 8 m − 8 m = 16 m − 8 m = 8 m
Divide the answer by 2: 8 m ÷ 2 = 4 m

This can also be illustrated with a part-whole model, if necessary. The length can also be doubled first and then subtracted, but mental computation is easier when subtracting the smaller number twice.

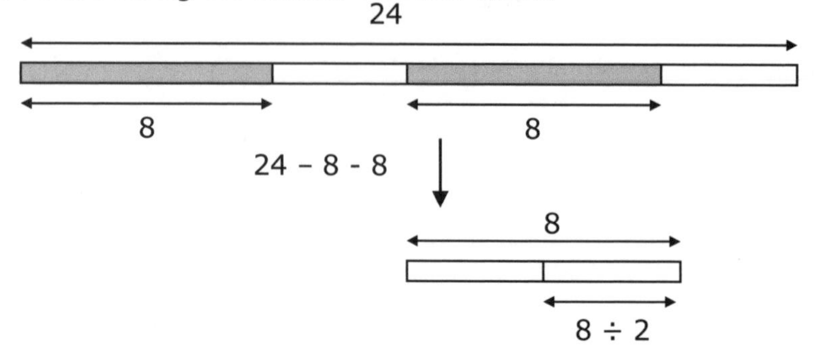

Provide other examples.

Learning Tasks 2-4, pp. 85-86

2. (a) Perimeter of square = 10 cm x 4 = 40 cm = perimeter of rectangle.
Length + width of rectangle = 40 cm ÷ 2 = 20 cm
Length of rectangle = 20 cm - 5 cm = **15 cm**
(b) Area of rectangle = 15 cm x 5 cm = 75 cm^2
Area of square = 10 cm x 10 cm = 100 cm^2
The **square** has a bigger area.

3. 5 25

4. 24

If necessary, review square numbers so that your student can recognize a number as a square number, and given such a number can find the number which when multiplied by itself gives the square number (the square root).

1 x 1 = 1
2 x 2 = 4
3 x 3 = 9
4 x 4 = 16
5 x 5 = 25
6 x 6 = 36
7 x 7 = 49
8 x 8 = 64
9 x 9 = 81
10 x 10 = 100
11 x 11 = 121
12 x 12 = 144

Learning Task 5, p. 86

Since length x width = area,
then width = area ÷ length
length = area ÷ width

So for this learning task, length = 40 m^2 ÷ 8 m = **5 m**

Once the length is found, we can find the perimeter.
Perimeter = **26 m**

Provide other examples if necessary.

Workbook Exercise 49

Part 2 Composite Figures

(1) Perimeter of Composite Figures (pp. 87-88)

> Find the perimeter of a figure made up of rectangles and/or squares.

Cut some paper or index cards into 3-4 different sized **rectangles and/or squares**, such as 3 cm by 5 cm, several 2 cm x 2 cm, 4 cm x 2 cm. Have your student arrange them various ways on centimeter graph paper so that adjacent rectangles touch at least 1 cm along the side of both. Let her find the perimeters of each arrangement. The most common method of finding the perimeter is to simply add all the sides.

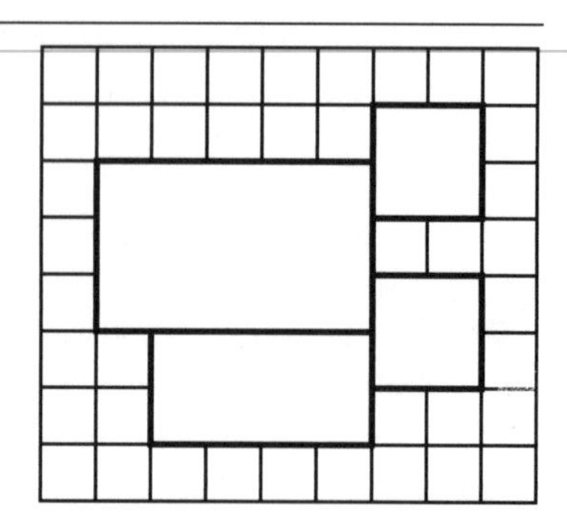

Page 87, Learning Tasks 1-2, p. 88

A - area = 22 cm^2, perimeter = 24 cm
B - area = 22 cm^2, perimeter = 20 cm
C - area = 22 cm^2, perimeter = 22 cm
D - area = 22 cm^2, perimeter = 24 cm
yes; no

1. **86**
2. **140**

Workbook Exercise 50

After your student has experience with these problems, you may want to point out a short-cut method for finding the perimeter. We can imagine the figure is formed from a rectangle with part of the sides "pushed in." The perimeter of the figure would be the same as that of the rectangle, plus some extra sides if one side of the rectangle was "pushed in" in the middle away from the corners.

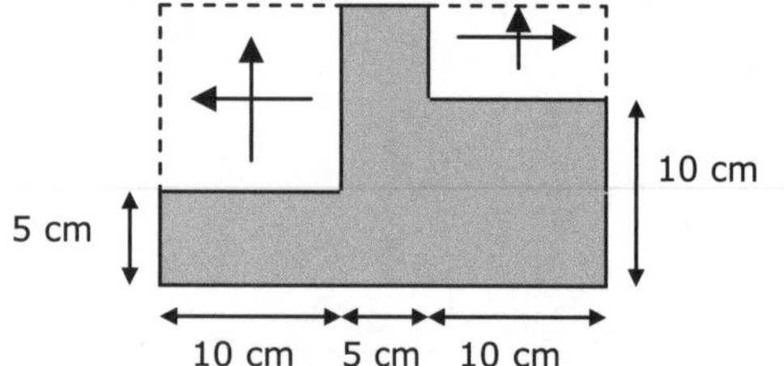

Perimeter of figure is the same as that of a rectangle with sides 25 cm and 15 cm.

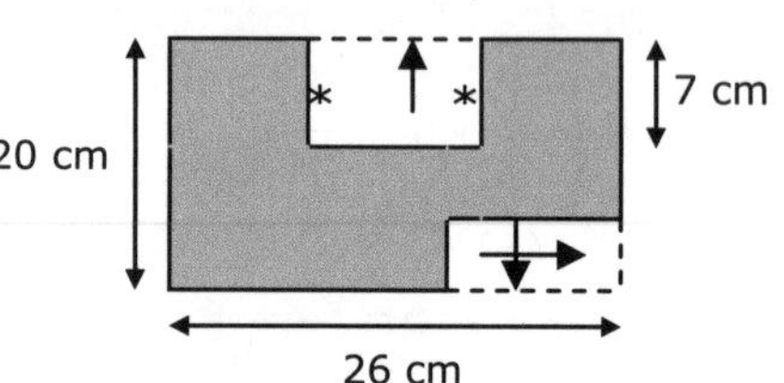

Perimeter of figure is the same as that of a rectangle with sides 26 cm and 20 cm, plus 2 x 7 cm for the starred sides.

(2) Area of Composite Figures (p. 89)

- Find the area of a figure made up of rectangles and/or squares.

Learning Tasks 3-4, p. 89

3. 90
4. 105

To find the areas of these figures, they must be broken up into rectangles and squares. Discuss other methods for each of these figures besides the one given in the text. Note that the area of shaded figures can sometimes be found by subtracting the area of a smaller square from a larger square around the entire figure.

Learning Task 3:
The figure could also be broken up into two squares 5 cm by 5 cm and one rectangle in the middle 4 cm by 10 cm.

Area = 25 m^2 + 25 m^2 + 40 m^2

Or, we could find the area of a large rectangle 14 m by 10 m, and then subtract the area of two smaller rectangles 5 m by 5 m.

Area = 140 m^2 – 25 m^2 – 25 m^2

Let your student see if he gets the same answer with different methods.

Learning Task 4:
The figure could be divided up into three rectangles two different ways. One would be to have the three rectangles: 3 m by 12 m, 4 m by 13 m, 3 m by 7 m (12 m – 5 m).

Area = 36 m^2 + 48 m^2 + 21 m^2

Workbook Exercise 51

(3) Area of Paths (p. 90)

➢ Find the area of a path around a rectangle.

In the previous section, the student learned that the area of a composite figure could be found by subtracting the area of a smaller rectangle from that of a bigger one. This is true even if the smaller rectangle is entirely within the larger rectangle. The difference is the area around the smaller rectangle.

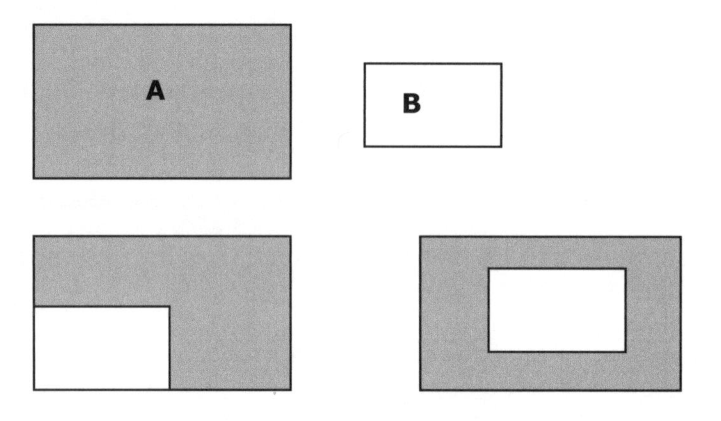

Area of shaded part = area of A – area of B

Cut out two rectangles from centimeter graph paper, one smaller than the other, for example 5 cm by 8 cm and 3 cm by 6 cm. Ask your student to find the difference in area of these two rectangles.

Area of larger rectangle = 5 cm x 8 cm = 40 cm^2
Area of smaller rectangle = 3 cm x 6 cm = 18 cm^2
Difference = 40 cm^2 – 18 cm^2 = 22 cm^2

Place the smaller rectangle on top of the other and move it around, showing that the difference in the area of the two is always 28 cm^2.

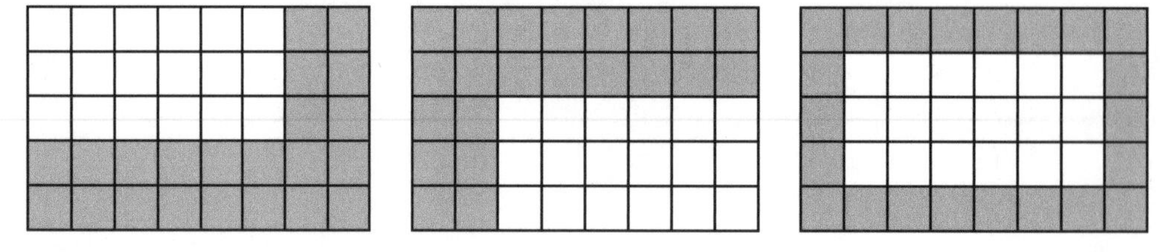

In the third figure above, the difference is the path around the smaller rectangle.

➤ Draw a figure, giving the dimensions of the smaller rectangle and the width of the path.

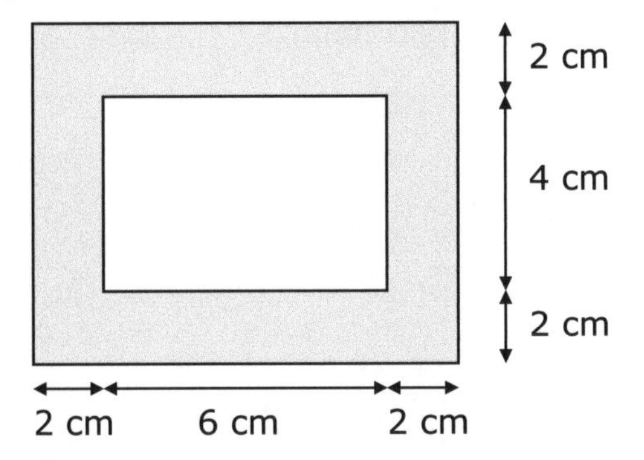

Ask your student to find the area of the larger rectangle. We first need to find the length and width.

Length of larger rectangle = 6 cm + 2 cm + 2 cm = 10 cm
Width of larger rectangle = 4 cm + 2 cm + 2 cm = 8 cm
Area of larger rectangle = 10 cm x 8 cm = 80 cm^2

Ask her to find the area of the "path" around the smaller rectangle, which is the difference in area of the two rectangles.

Area of smaller rectangle = 6 cm x 4 cm = 24 cm^2
Area of "path" = 80 cm^2 - 24 cm^2 = 56 cm^2

Discuss other ways of finding this path. It can be found by dividing it up into smaller rectangles, such as two rectangles that are 10 cm by 2 cm and two that are 4 cm by 2 cm, and adding the areas together.

20 cm + 20 cm + 8 cm + 8 cm = 56 cm^2

Ask which way is easier for finding the area of the path.

Learning Tasks 5-6, p. 90

5. Area of big rectangle = **80** m^2
   Area of small rectangle = 6 m x 8 m = **48** m^2
   Area of path = 80 m^2 - 48 m^2 = **32** m^2

6. Area of big rectangle = **120** m^2
   Length of small rectangle = 12 m - 2 m - 3 m = **7** m
   Width of small rectangle = 10 m - 2 m - 2 m = **6** m
   Area of small rectangle = 7 m x 6 m = **42** m^2
   Area of shaded part = 120 m^2 - 42 m^2 = **78** m^2

Workbook Exercise 52

(4) Practice (pp. 91-93)

➢ Practice problems involving area and perimeter.

Practice 7A, pp 91-93

1. (a) 8 cm, 96 cm^2 (b) 15 cm, 120 cm^2
   (c) 14 m, 84 m^2 (d) 11m, 165 m^2

2. (a) 6 m, 18 m (b) 4 m, 24 m
   (c) 16 cm, 44 cm (d) 12 cm, 42 cm

3. (a) 40 cm^2, 28 cm (b) 59 m^2, 40 m
   (c) 168 m^2, 68 m (d) 483 m^2, 112 m

4. (a) 440 m^2 (b) 225 m^2

5. Height = 36 m^2 ÷ 9 m = **4 m**

6. 704 cm^2

7. 80 m^2

8. 912 cm^2

9. 30 m^2

Review

Review C, pp. 94-96

1. (a) 741 (b) 1056 (c) 396
   (d) 6448 (e) 14,336 (f) 1188

2. 18

3. (a) Any 3: $\frac{4}{6}, \frac{6}{9}, \frac{8}{12}, \frac{10}{15}, \frac{12}{18}...$
   (b) Any 3: $\frac{2}{10}, \frac{3}{15}, \frac{4}{20}, \frac{5}{25}, \frac{6}{30}...$
   (c) Any 3: $\frac{3}{4}, \frac{18}{24}, \frac{27}{36}..., \frac{6}{8}, \frac{12}{16}...$

4. (a) $\frac{2}{3}, \frac{3}{4}, \frac{5}{6}$ (b) $1\frac{7}{10}, \frac{7}{4}, 2$

5. (a) $\frac{3}{4}$ (b) $\frac{3}{4}$ (c) $\frac{2}{5}$

6. (a) $>$ (b) $=$ (c) $>$

7. Length = 78 m^2 ÷ 6 m = **13 m**
   Perimeter = 13 m + 13 m + 6 m + 6 m = **38 m**

8. Side = 48 cm ÷ 4 = 12 cm
   Area = 12 cm x 12 cm = **144 cm^2**

9. (a) 156 m^2 (b) 108 m^2

10. (a) Perimeter = **110 cm**; Area = **460 cm^2**
    (b) Perimeter = **60 m**; Area = **128 m^2**

11. (a) A and C (b) B and C (c) C

12. X and Z, Z

13. check student's bar graph

14. 11 years 2 months, 154 cm, 41 kg
    11 years 10 months, 153 cm, 44 kg
    13 years 8 months, 160 cm, 48 kg

US› 15. Amount Roger used = $4\frac{2}{5} - \frac{3}{10} = 4\frac{4}{10} - \frac{3}{10} = 4\frac{1}{10}$ yd

Total amount of rope used = $4\frac{4}{10} + 4\frac{1}{10} = 8\frac{5}{10} = \mathbf{8\frac{1}{2}}$ **yd**

3d› 15. Amount Rohan used = $4\frac{2}{5} - \frac{3}{10} = 4\frac{4}{10} - \frac{3}{10} = 4\frac{1}{10}$ m

Total amount of rope used = $4\frac{4}{10} + 4\frac{1}{10} = 8\frac{5}{10} = \mathbf{8\frac{1}{2}}$ **m**

US› 16. Total amount cut = 75 in. x 12 = 900 in.
Length remaining = 1250 in. – 900 in. = **350 in.**

3d› 16. Total amount cut = 75 cm x 12 = 900 cm
Length remaining = 1250 cm – 900 cm = **350 cm**

17. There are 13 units.
11 more units of people took part in the walkathon than in the swimming competition.
11 units = 45 x 11 = **495**

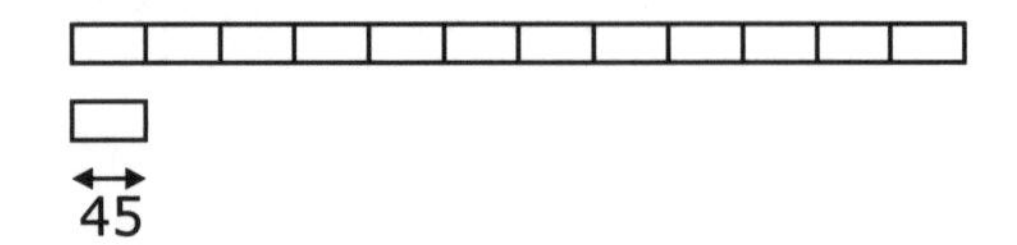

18. Total mangoes = 138 x 24 = 3312
Amount sold = 3312 – 72 = 3240
Amount each bought = 3240 ÷ 3 = **1080**

Workbook Review 4

Answers to Workbook Exercises and Reviews

Exercise 1

1. (a) 4,053 (b) 23,405
2. (a) thirty-two thousand, four hundred (b) 32,400
3. (a) 8,402 (b) 12,793 (c) 90,511 (d) 88,008 (e) 99,999
4. (a) two thousand, eighty dollars
   (b) nine thousand, two hundred fifteen dollars
   (c) forty-seven thousand, ten dollars
   (d) eighty-nine thousand, one hundred two dollars
   (e) forty thousand, nine hundred dollars
   (f) seventy-eight thousand, nine hundred ninety-nine dollars

---

Exercise 2

1. (a) 9000; 11,000
   (b) 6400; 8400
   (c) 34,065; 44,065
   (d) 20,200; 25,200
   (e) 10,043; 10,243
2. (a) 9
20
500
3000
20,000
   (b) 8
10
600
0
40,000
   (c) 3
20
0
5000
40,000
   (d) 8
80
800
8000
80,000
3. (a) 3 (b) 6000 (c) 40,000 (d) 2000 (e) 100
4. (a) 4307 (b) 56,400 (c) 30,768 (d) 11,400 (e) 90,090
5. (a) 43,628 (b) 25,324 (c) 89,900 (d) 86,100
   (e) 100 (f) 1000 (g) 1000 (h) 10
6. (a) 526 (b) 30,000

Exercise 3

1. (a) 70,000 (b) 2; 200 (c) 4; 8
2. (a) 4000 (b) 4; 40,000 (c) 500
3. (a) 3695; 3956; 30,965; 35,096
   (b) 29,687; 43,526; 46,254; 50,314

Exercise 4

1. (a) 16,000 (b) 37,000 (c) 24,000 (d) 41,000 (e) 70,000
2. (a) 9000 (b) 34,000 (c) 24,000 (d) 33,000 (e) 24,000
3. (a) 6000 (b) 48,000 (c) 63,000 (d) 42,000 (e) 90,000
4. (a) 2000 (b) 12,000 (c) 3000 (d) 3000 (e) 12,000

Exercise 5

1. (a) 50 (b) 80 (c) 160
   (d) 300 (e) 1640 (f) 3450
2. (a) $110 (b) $280
   (c) $1260 (d) $2040
3. 440; 270; 100; 600; 350; 270

Exercise 6

1. (a) 100 (b) 600 (c) 1000
   (d) 1400 (e) 1900 (f) 2900
2. (a) 800 (b) 3200 (c) $2500 (d) 6300 km
3. 700; 700; 2000; 5800; 1200; 2100

Exercise 7

1. (a) 900
   (b) 300
   (c) 800 + 200 = 1000
   (d) 900 - 300 = 600
   (e) 600 + 600 = 1200
   (f) 900 - 300 = 600
   (g) 1800 + 400 = 2200
   (h) 2300 - 1000 = 1300
2. (a) 800
   (b) 700 - 200 - 300 = 200
   (c) 1000 - 200 + 100 = 900
   (d) 500 + 300 - 300 = 500
   (e) 2000 - 600 + 500 = 1900
   (f) 2400 + 600 - 700 = 2300
   (g) 1100 - 100 + 400 = 1400
   (h) 3000 + 1000 + 400 = 4400

Exercise 8

1. 1, 2, 4, 5, 10, 20
2. (a) 2, 6 (b) 1, 8 (c) 3, 7
3. (a) 4 (b) 3
   (c) 9 (d) 8
   (e) 8 (f) 8
   (g) 9 (h) 9
   (i) 10 (j) 8
4. (a) 8, 4; 1, 2, 4, 8
   (b) 15, 5; 1, 3, 5, 15

Exercise 9

1. (a) no (b) yes
2. yes yes no
   yes yes no
   yes yes yes
   yes no yes
   yes yes no
3. (a) yes (b) no (c) yes
4. (a) 1, 2, 4, 8, 16, 32, 64
   (b) 1, 2, 3, 4, 6, 8, 9, 12, 18, 24, 36, 72
   (c) 1, 2, 3, 4, 6, 7, 12, 14, 21, 28, 42, 84

Exercise 10

1. (a) 6, 12, 18, 24 (b) 7, 14, 21, 28, 35
2. 6, 8, 10, 12, 14
   9, 12, 15, 18, 21
   12, 16, 20, 24, 28
   18, 24, 30, 36, 42
   24, 32, 40, 48, 56
   30, 40, 50, 60, 70
3. (a) 6, 12 (b) 8, 16
   (c) 9, 18, 27, 36, ...
   6, 12, 18, 24, 30, 36, ...
   18, 36
   (d) 8, 16, 24, 32, 40, 48, ...
   6, 12, 18, 24, 30, 36, 42, 48 ...
   24, 48

Exercise 11

1. (a) 8000; 7572
   (b) 4000; 28,000; 28,252
   (c) 6000; 48,000; 47,896
   (d) 8000; 72,000; 73,755

Exercise 12

1. (a) 500; 495
   (b) 3600, 600, 599
   (c) 4200, 600, 602
   (d) 6300, 700, 720

2. | | | | |
   |---|---|---|---|
   | 12,096 | 11,850 | 28,872 | 43,488 |
   | 1302 | 3069 | 242 | 252 |

Exercise 13

1. There are 4 units of beads total
   1 unit = 1875
   4 units = 1875 x 4 = 7500
   There are **7500** beads.

   red
   white
   1875
   ?

2. There are 4 units of meat buns and 1 unit of curry buns.
   There are 3 more units of meat buns than curry buns.
   4 units = 4864
   1 unit = 4864 ÷ 4 = 1216
   3 units = 1216 x 3 = 3648
   There are **3648** more meat buns than curry buns.

   4864
   meat
   curry
   ?

3. Amount spent on computers
   = $3569 x 2 = $7138
   Total money
   = $7138 + $2907 = **$10,045**

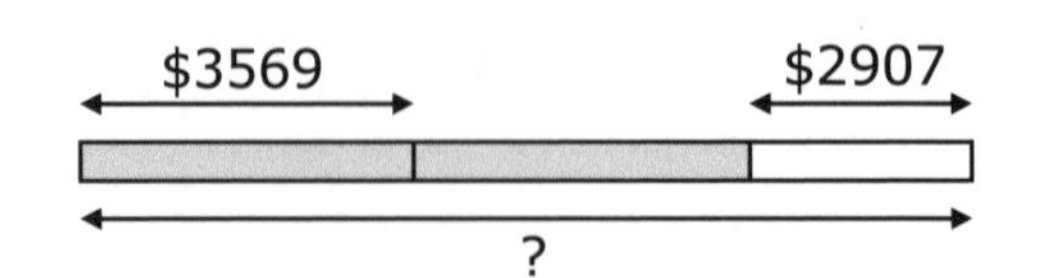

4. Amount 2 people received
   = 2 x 4356 = $8712
   Amount 3 people received
   = 3 x $3807 = $11,421
   Total
   = $8712 + $11,421 = **$20,133**

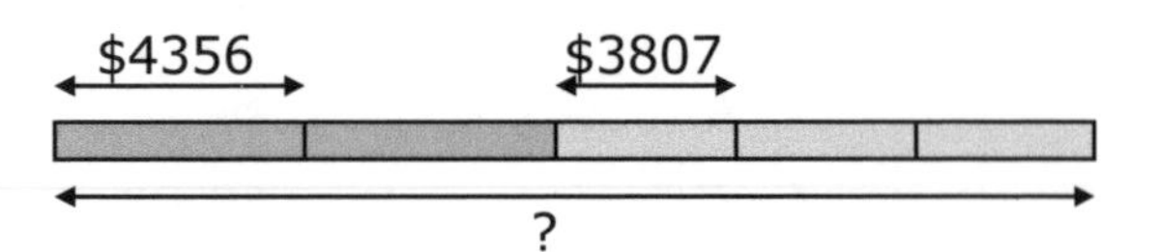

Exercise 14

1. 80 $340   5860

2.	260	380	5820	7490
	204	2040	200	2000
	1744	17,440	5360	53,600

Exercise 15

1. (a) 120; 120 (across)
   1200; 1200
   1200; 1200
   12,000; 12,000
   12,000; 12,000
   (b) 30
   300; 300
   3000; 3000
   3000; 3000
   30,000; 30,000
   30,000; 30,000
2. (a) 2000; 2028
   (b) 80 x 30 = 2400; 2574
   (c) 30 x 90 = 2700; 2523
   (d) 90 x 70 = 6300; 6532
3. (a) 8000; 8066
   (b) 500 x 60 = 30,000; 28,497
   (c) 400 x 60 = 24,000; 23,808
   (d) 600 x 80 = 48,000; 50,544

Exercise 16

1.	B 273	D 663	F 888	G 6560
	A 868	B 2385	C 3540	E 686

2.	A 2714	C 7719	D 5922
	F 2839	H 1518	J 6225
	A 27,745	B 41,912	E 9688
	F 21,518	G 3451	I 8775

Review 1

1. (a) 55,382 (b) 40,012
2. (a) Twenty-eight thousand, seven hundred forty
   (b) Thirty-five thousand, eighty-four
3. 38,615; 68,615

4. (a) 8000 (b) 10,501 (c) 67,000
5. 7000
6. 0
7. \$10,312 - \$8000 = \$**2312**
8. 11,230; 11,290
9. \$90,400
10. Any 2: 1, 2, 3, 4, 6, 9, 12, 18, 36
11. Any 2: 30, 60, 90, 120, 150
12. ___ x 8 = 216 → 216 ÷ 8 = **27**
13. Total apples = 50 x 24 = 1200
    Put them in groups of 3: 1200 ÷ 3 = 400
    If each group of 3 sells for \$1, 400 groups sell for **\$400**

Exercise 17

1. (a) $\frac{3}{5}$ (b) $\frac{7}{8}$
   (c) $\frac{5}{6}$ (d) $\frac{7}{10}$

2. (a) 1 (b) $\frac{1}{2}$ (c) $\frac{2}{3}$
   (d) $\frac{3}{5}$ (e) $\frac{5}{6}$ (f) $\frac{5}{7}$
   (g) $\frac{3}{4}$ (h) $\frac{7}{9}$ (i) $\frac{9}{10}$

3. (clockwise) $\frac{1}{2}, \frac{2}{3}, \frac{1}{4}, \frac{3}{5}, \frac{5}{6}, \frac{3}{8}, \frac{3}{10}, \frac{7}{9}$

4. (a) $\frac{3}{5}$ (b) 1
   (c) $\frac{5}{8}$ (d) $\frac{7}{9}$
   (e) $\frac{6}{7}$ (f) 1
   (g) $\frac{3}{5}$ (h) $\frac{3}{4}$

Exercise 18

1. (a) $\frac{5}{12}$ (b) $\frac{4}{8}$; $\frac{7}{8}$ (c) $\frac{4}{10}$; $\frac{7}{10}$

2. $\frac{1}{2}+\frac{1}{4}=\frac{2}{4}+\frac{1}{4}=\mathbf{\frac{3}{4}}$ $\frac{1}{6}+\frac{2}{3}=\frac{1}{6}+\frac{4}{6}=\mathbf{\frac{5}{6}}$

   $\frac{2}{9}+\frac{2}{3}=\frac{2}{9}+\frac{6}{9}=\mathbf{\frac{8}{9}}$ $\frac{1}{9}+\frac{1}{3}=\frac{1}{9}+\frac{3}{9}=\mathbf{\frac{4}{9}}$

   $\frac{1}{5}+\frac{1}{10}=\frac{2}{10}+\frac{1}{10}=\mathbf{\frac{3}{10}}$ $\frac{3}{10}+\frac{1}{5}=\frac{3}{10}+\frac{2}{10}=\frac{5}{10}=\mathbf{\frac{1}{2}}$

   $\frac{1}{8}+\frac{3}{4}=\frac{1}{8}+\frac{6}{8}=\mathbf{\frac{7}{8}}$ $\frac{3}{8}+\frac{1}{4}=\frac{3}{8}+\frac{2}{8}=\mathbf{\frac{5}{8}}$

   $\frac{1}{12}+\frac{2}{3}=\frac{1}{12}+\frac{8}{12}=\frac{9}{12}=\mathbf{\frac{3}{4}}$ $\frac{1}{4}+\frac{1}{12}=\frac{3}{12}+\frac{1}{12}=\frac{4}{12}=\mathbf{\frac{1}{3}}$

Exercise 19

1. (a) $\frac{3}{5}$ (b) $\frac{1}{6}$

   (c) $\frac{3}{8}$ (d) $\frac{3}{10}$

   (e) $\frac{1}{4}$ (f) $\frac{3}{5}$

2. (a) $\frac{1}{3}$ (b) $\frac{2}{5}$

   (c) $\frac{2}{3}$ (d) $\frac{5}{8}$

   (e) $\frac{1}{4}$ (f) $\frac{3}{4}$

   (g) $\frac{3}{5}$ (h) $\frac{3}{10}$

   (i) $\frac{1}{2}$ (j) $\frac{1}{12}$

3. (clockwise from top) $\frac{1}{2}$, $\frac{1}{8}$, $\frac{5}{7}$, $\frac{3}{10}$, $\frac{1}{4}$, $\frac{1}{6}$, $\frac{3}{5}$, $\frac{2}{3}$

4. (a) $\frac{1}{2}$ (b) $\frac{2}{7}$ (c) 0 (d) 0

   (e) $\frac{1}{2}$ (f) $\frac{1}{3}$ (g) $\frac{3}{5}$ (h) $\frac{1}{3}$

Exercise 20

1. (a) $\frac{1}{4}$ (b) $\frac{4}{6}$; $\frac{1}{6}$ (c) $\frac{8}{12}$; $\frac{7}{12}$

2. A $\frac{1}{2}-\frac{1}{6}=\frac{3}{6}-\frac{1}{6}=\mathbf{\frac{1}{3}}$

   D $\frac{3}{4}-\frac{5}{8}=\frac{6}{8}-\frac{5}{8}=\mathbf{\frac{1}{8}}$

   E $\frac{2}{3}-\frac{2}{9}=\frac{6}{9}-\frac{2}{9}=\mathbf{\frac{4}{9}}$

   I $\frac{3}{4}-\frac{1}{12}=\frac{9}{12}-\frac{1}{12}=\frac{8}{12}=\mathbf{\frac{2}{3}}$

   L $\frac{2}{5}-\frac{1}{10}=\frac{4}{10}-\frac{1}{10}=\mathbf{\frac{3}{10}}$

   Q $\frac{5}{6}=\frac{5}{12}+\frac{10}{12}-\frac{5}{12}=\mathbf{\frac{5}{12}}$

   R $\frac{4}{5}-\frac{3}{10}=\frac{8}{10}-\frac{3}{10}=\frac{5}{10}=\mathbf{\frac{1}{2}}$

   T $\frac{1}{2}-\frac{5}{12}=\frac{6}{12}-\frac{5}{12}=\mathbf{\frac{1}{12}}$

   U $\frac{7}{12}-\frac{1}{3}=\frac{7}{12}-\frac{4}{12}=\frac{3}{12}=\mathbf{\frac{1}{4}}$

   QUADRILATERAL

Exercise 21

1. Fraction of cloth left = $1-\frac{3}{8}=\mathbf{\frac{5}{8}}$

2. Difference = $\frac{3}{4}\text{m}-\frac{5}{12}\text{m}=\frac{9}{12}\text{m}-\frac{5}{12}\text{m}=\frac{4}{12}\text{m}=\mathbf{\frac{1}{3}\ m}$

3. Fraction spent = $\frac{1}{2}+\frac{1}{6}=\frac{3}{6}+\frac{1}{6}=\frac{4}{6}=\mathbf{\frac{2}{3}}$

4. Amount Jim drank $=\frac{3}{10}\ell-\frac{1}{5}\ell$

   $=\frac{3}{10}\ell-\frac{2}{10}\ell=\frac{1}{10}\ell$

   Mary $\frac{3}{10}$

   Jim $\frac{1}{5}$

   Total both drank $=\frac{3}{10}\ell+\frac{1}{10}\ell=\frac{4}{10}\ell=\mathbf{\frac{2}{5}}$ **liter**

US› 5. Ribbon left = 1 yd - $\frac{1}{2}$yd - $\frac{3}{10}$yd = $\frac{10}{10}$ yd - $\frac{5}{10}$yd - $\frac{3}{10}$yd = $\frac{2}{10}$ yd = $\mathbf{\frac{1}{5}}$ **yd**

3d› 5. Ribbon left = 1 m - $\frac{1}{2}$m - $\frac{3}{10}$m = $\frac{10}{10}$m - $\frac{5}{10}$m - $\frac{3}{10}$m = $\frac{2}{10}$m = $\mathbf{\frac{1}{5}}$ **m**

Exercise 22

1. (a) $3\frac{1}{2}$ (b) $2\frac{4}{5}$ (c) $2\frac{1}{6}$ (d) $3\frac{7}{8}$
2. (a) $1\frac{3}{5}$; $2\frac{2}{5}$ (b) $3\frac{1}{5}$ (c) $3\frac{3}{4}$ (d) $2\frac{2}{3}$

Exercise 23

1. (a) $\frac{6}{3}$ (b) $\frac{8}{4}$ (c) $\frac{11}{16}$ (d) $\frac{13}{5}$
2. (b) $2\frac{4}{9}$; $\frac{22}{9}$ (c) $1\frac{2}{3}$; $\frac{5}{3}$ (d) $3\frac{3}{4}$; $\frac{15}{4}$
   (e) $2\frac{3}{5}$; $\frac{13}{5}$ (f) $2\frac{7}{8}$; $\frac{23}{8}$

Exercise 24

1. (a) $2\frac{3}{4}$ (b) $3\frac{3}{5}$
2. $1\frac{2}{3}$; $2\frac{1}{3}$; 3; $3\frac{2}{3}$
3. (a) $2\frac{1}{2}$ (b) $1\frac{7}{10}$ (c) $1\frac{1}{6}$ (d) $2\frac{1}{3}$
   (e) $2\frac{1}{5}$ (f) $2\frac{1}{4}$ (g) $1\frac{3}{8}$ (h) $4\frac{1}{2}$
   (i) 3 (j) 4

Exercise 25

1. (a) 6 (b) 6; 8
2. (a) $\frac{11}{6}$ (b) $\frac{19}{8}$
3. (a) $\frac{7}{5}$ (b) $\frac{5}{4}$ (c) $\frac{19}{8}$ (d) $\frac{21}{10}$
   (e) $\frac{19}{6}$ (f) $\frac{10}{3}$ (g) $\frac{5}{2}$ (h) $\frac{23}{5}$
   (i) $\frac{13}{9}$ (j) $\frac{29}{12}$
4. $\frac{4}{4}$; $\frac{7}{4}$; $\frac{9}{4}$; $\frac{11}{4}$; $\frac{14}{4}$

5. $1\frac{1}{3} \to \frac{4}{3}$, $1\frac{1}{4} \to \frac{5}{4}$, $1\frac{1}{5} \to \frac{6}{5}$, $1\frac{1}{6} \to \frac{7}{6}$, $1\frac{1}{7} \to \frac{8}{7}$,
$1\frac{1}{8} \to \frac{9}{8}$, $1\frac{1}{9} \to \frac{10}{9}$, $2\frac{2}{3} \to \frac{8}{3}$, $2\frac{1}{2} \to \frac{5}{2}$, $1\frac{3}{4} \to \frac{7}{4}$,
$2\frac{1}{5} \to \frac{11}{5}$, $1\frac{5}{6} \to \frac{11}{6}$, $1\frac{7}{8} \to \frac{15}{8}$

Exercise 26

1. (a) 3 (b) $2\frac{1}{2}$ (c) 3
   (d) $2\frac{2}{3}$ (e) $6\frac{1}{3}$ (f) $3\frac{1}{3}$

2. $3\frac{7}{4} \to 4\frac{3}{4}$, $3\frac{1}{2} \to 2\frac{3}{2}$, $2\frac{2}{5} \to 1\frac{7}{5}$, $2\frac{1}{3} \to 1\frac{4}{3}$, $3\frac{1}{4} \to 2\frac{5}{4}$, $4\frac{1}{6} \to 3\frac{7}{6}$

3. (a) 1 (b) 1 (c) $1\frac{1}{2}$ (d) $1\frac{2}{7}$
   (e) $1\frac{1}{3}$ (f) $1\frac{1}{8}$ (g) $1\frac{1}{6}$ (h) $1\frac{1}{10}$

4. (a) $\frac{2}{9}$ (b) $\frac{7}{12}$ (c) $1\frac{1}{4}$ (d) $1\frac{3}{8}$
   (e) $2\frac{3}{7}$ (f) $\frac{1}{5}$

5. (a) $>$ (b) $<$ (c) $<$ (d) $=$
   (e) $<$ (f) $<$ (g) $=$ (h) $>$
   (i) $>$ (j) $=$

Review 2

1. (a) sixty thousand, five hundred
   (b) forty-two thousand, eight hundred nineteen
2. (a) 75,612 (b) 80,002
3. 3000
4. 10,000
5. 80,036; 80,360; 83,060; 83,600; 86,300
6. 6300
7. 6, 12, 18, 24, 30
8. 4
9. 1840

10. 210
11. 622 r2
12. $\frac{5}{12}, \frac{3}{4}, 1, \frac{7}{6}$
13. Draw a line down the middle. There are 8 sections (triangles) and two are shaded. The fraction shaded = $\frac{2}{8} = \mathbf{\frac{1}{4}}$
14. 5345
15. $\frac{7}{4}$
16. $4\frac{4}{5}$
17. Amount earned in 6 months = 6 x $1750 = **$10,500**
18. Number of bags = 1188 ÷ 6 = **198**

US› 19. 600 is added to the number of stickers Tasha has, they will both have the same amount; the total will be two units.
2 units = 2000 + 600 = 2600
1 unit = 2600 ÷ 2 = 1300
Nicole has **1300** stickers.

3d› 19. 600 is added to the number of stickers Suhua has, they will both have the same amount; the total will be two units.
2 units = 2000 + 600 = 2600
1 unit = 2600 ÷ 2 = 1300
Meifen has **1300** stickers.

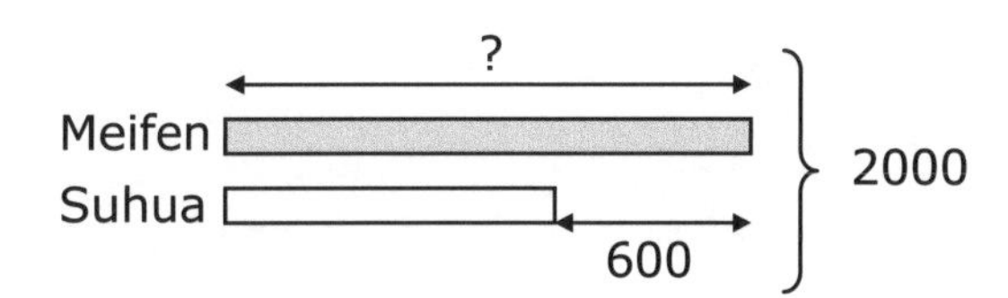

20. Cost of 12 chairs = 12 x $165 = $1980
Cost of table = $2400 - $1980 = **$420**

21. adults = 4 units
children = 1 unit
5 units = 2500
1 unit = 2500 ÷ 5 = 500
4 units = 500 x 4 = 2000 = number of adults
Number of women = 2000 – 1200 = **800**

22. Cost of hi-fi set = \$1980 + \$1200 = \$3180
    Cost of both = \$1980 + \$3180 = \$5160
    Amount each person paid = \$5160 ÷ 4 = **\$1290**

23. Total oranges bought = 25 x 36 = 900
    Oranges left = 900 – 28 – 786 = **86**

24. Total orange juice = 12 x 375 ml = 4500 ml
    Capacity of two 2 liter jugs = 2 x 2000 ml = 4000 ml
    Amount left after pouring into jugs = 4500 ml – 4000 ml = **500 ml**

25. (a) Total amount used = $\frac{2}{5}$kg + $\frac{3}{10}$kg = $\frac{4}{10}$kg + $\frac{3}{10}$kg = $\mathbf{\frac{7}{10}}$ **kg**

    (b) Difference in amounts used = $\frac{4}{10}$kg – $\frac{3}{10}$kg = $\mathbf{\frac{1}{10}}$ **kg**

Exercise 27

1. (a) 8 each set
   (b) 6 each set

2. (a) $\frac{2}{7}$ (b) $\frac{2}{3}$ (c) $\frac{3}{4}$ (d) $\frac{3}{7}$

3. (a) $\frac{2}{5}$; $\frac{3}{5}$ (b) $\frac{1}{2}$; $\frac{1}{6}$; $\frac{1}{3}$ (c) $\frac{1}{2}$

Exercise 28

1. 5; 15 2. 5; 15
3. 7; 14 4. 3; 21
5. 2; 6 6. 4; 20

Exercise 29

1. (a) 2 (b) 3
   (c) 4 (d) 4
   (e) 9 (f) 9

2. (a) 4 (b) 5 (c) 5 (d) 3
   (e) 16 (f) 16 (g) 15 (h) 15

3. (a) $\frac{2}{3} \times 15 = 2 \times \frac{1}{3} \times 15$
   $= 2 \times \frac{15}{3}$
   $= 2 \times 5$
   $= \mathbf{10}$

   (b) $\frac{3}{4} \times 20 = 3 \times \frac{20}{4}$
   $= 3 \times 5$
   $= \mathbf{15}$

(c) $\frac{4}{5} \times 30 = 4 \times \frac{30}{5}$
$= 4 \times 6$
$= \mathbf{24}$

(d) $\frac{5}{6} \times 36 = 5 \times \frac{36}{6}$
$= 5 \times 6$
$= \mathbf{30}$

(e) $\frac{2}{3} \times 48 = 2 \times \frac{48}{3}$
$= 2 \times 16$
$= \mathbf{32}$

(f) $\frac{3}{4} \times 60 = 3 \times \frac{60}{4}$
$= 3 \times 15$
$= \mathbf{45}$

(g) $\frac{3}{5} \times 100 = 3 \times \frac{100}{5}$
$= 3 \times 20$
$= \mathbf{60}$

(h) $\frac{7}{10} \times 120 = 7 \times \frac{120}{10}$
$= 7 \times 12$
$= \mathbf{84}$

Exercise 30

1. (a) $4\frac{1}{2}$ (b) $2\frac{2}{3}$ (c) $1\frac{3}{4}$
   (d) $3\frac{3}{4}$ (e) $7\frac{1}{2}$ (f) $3\frac{3}{4}$

2. (a) $\frac{1}{3} \times 10 = \frac{10}{3} = \mathbf{3\frac{1}{3}}$
   (b) $\frac{1}{5} \times 9 = \frac{9}{5} = \mathbf{1\frac{4}{5}}$
   (c) $\frac{1}{6} \times 10 = \mathbf{1\frac{2}{3}}$
   (d) $\frac{1}{8} \times 20 = \frac{20}{8} = \mathbf{2\frac{1}{2}}$
   (e) $\frac{5}{6} \times 5 = 5 \times \frac{5}{6}$
   $= \frac{25}{6}$
   $= \mathbf{4\frac{1}{6}}$
   (f) $\frac{5}{8} \times 9 = 5 \times \frac{9}{8}$
   $= 5 \times 1\frac{1}{8}$
   $= \mathbf{5\frac{5}{8}}$
   (g) $\frac{5}{9} \times 3 = 5 \times \frac{3}{9}$
   $= 5 \times \frac{1}{3}$
   $= \frac{5}{3}$
   $= \mathbf{1\frac{2}{3}}$
   (h) $\frac{3}{10} \times 8 = 3 \times \frac{8}{10}$
   $= 3 \times \frac{4}{5}$
   $= \frac{12}{5}$
   $= \mathbf{2\frac{2}{5}}$

Exercise 31

1. (a) 5 units = 25; 1 unit = 25 ÷ 5 = 5
   Amount he gave to his friends = 2 units = 5 x 2 = **10**
   (b) Amount he had left = 3 units = 5 x 3 = **15**

2. (a) 8 units = $40; 1 unit = $40 ÷ 8 = $5,
   Cost of storybook = 3 units = $5 x 3 = **$15**
   (b) Amount she had left = 5 units = $5 x 5 = **$25** (or, $40 - $15 = $25)

3. 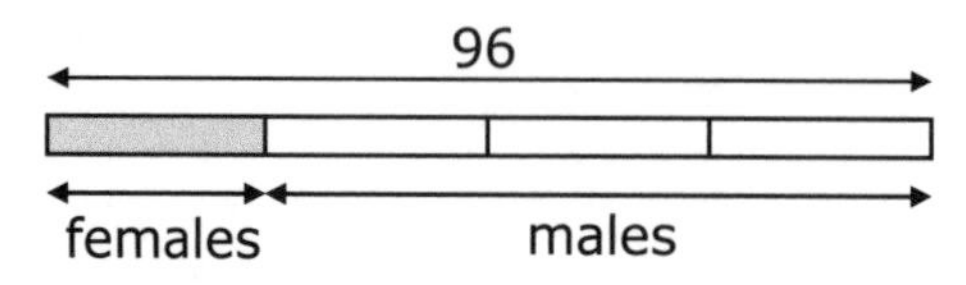

   4 units = 96
   1 unit = 96 ÷ 4 = 24
   (a) Number of females = 1 unit = **24**
   (b) Number of males = 3 units = 24 x 3 = **72**

4. 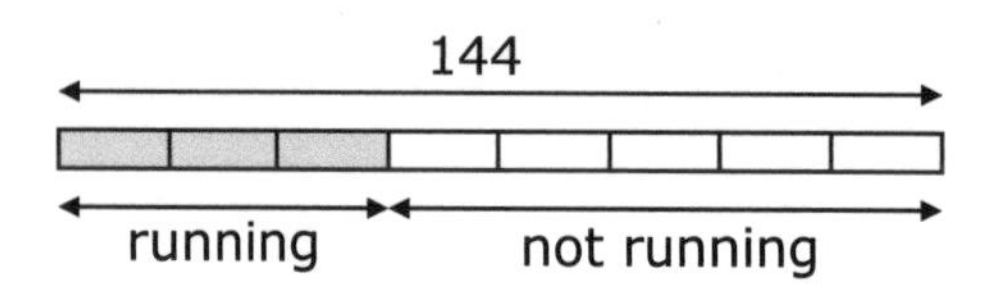

   8 units = 144
   1 unit = 144 ÷ 8 = 18
   (a) Number of children running = 3 units = 18 x 3 = **54**
   (b) Number of children not running = 5 units = 18 x 5 = **90**

Exercise 32

1. (a) $\frac{1}{5}$ (b) $\frac{80}{100} = \mathbf{\frac{4}{5}}$ (c) $\frac{25}{60} = \mathbf{\frac{5}{12}}$
2. (a) $\frac{8}{24} = \mathbf{\frac{1}{3}}$ (b) $\frac{50}{90} = \mathbf{\frac{5}{9}}$ (c) $\frac{45}{100} = \mathbf{\frac{9}{20}}$
3. $\frac{75}{100} = \mathbf{\frac{3}{4}}$
4. $\frac{16}{40} = \mathbf{\frac{2}{5}}$
5. $\frac{15}{40} = \mathbf{\frac{3}{8}}$
6. $\frac{24}{60} = \mathbf{\frac{2}{5}}$

Exercise 33

1. (a) 7 units = \$42; 1 unit = \$42 ÷ 7 = \$6
   Amount of money he had at first = 10 units = \$6 x 10 = **\$60**
   (b) Amount of money he saved = \$6 x 3 = **\$18**

2. (a) 3 units = 18; 1 unit = 18 ÷ 3 = 6
   Total number of children = 7 units = 6 x 7 = **42**
   (b) Number of girls = 4 units = 6 x 4 = **24**

3. 1 unit = 6 kg
   Amount of flour she bought = 6 kg x 3 = **18 kg**

4. 3 units = \$9; 1 unit = \$9 ÷ 3 = \$3
   Total money = 10 units = \$3 x 10 = **\$30**

Exercise 34

1. 5 units = \$25; 1 unit = \$25 ÷ 5 = \$5
   Amount she saved = 4 units = \$5 x 4 = **\$20**

2. He had $\frac{2}{5}$ of the oranges left.

   Number of oranges left = $\frac{2}{5}$ x 45 = **18**

3. Amount spent on calculator = $\frac{1}{4}$ x \$48 = \$12

   Total spent = \$12 + \$14 = **\$26**

4. Number of children = $\frac{2}{5}$ x 60 = 24

   Number of girls = 24 – 15 = **9**

Exercise 35

1. Number of mangoes sold = $\frac{3}{4}$ x 160 = 120

   Money received = \$2 x 120 = **\$240**

2. Amount of material used for curtains = $\frac{3}{5}$ x 30 m = 18 m

   Amount used for each curtain = 18 m ÷ 6 = **3 m**

US› 3. Amount of ribbon bought
= 5 units
= 5 ft x 5 = **40 ft**

3d› 3. Amount of ribbon bought
= 5 units
= 5 m x 5 = **40 m**

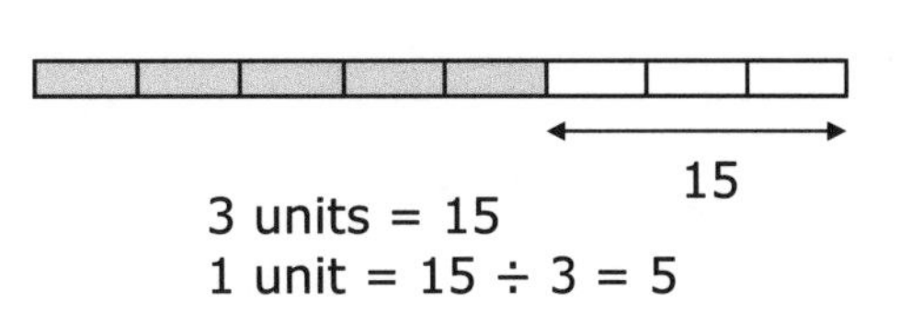

3 units = 15
1 unit = 15 ÷ 3 = 5

4. Number of stamps he used
   = 3 units
   = 6 x 3 = **18**

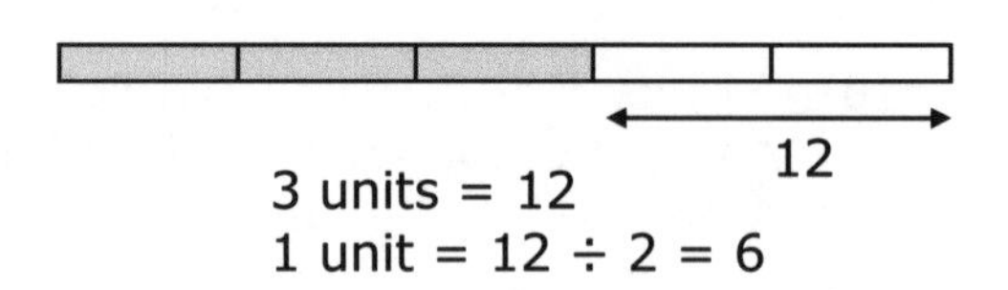

3 units = 12
1 unit = 12 ÷ 2 = 6

Review 3

1. 56,952
2. 85,320
3. 76,410
4. 6
5. 8; 16; 24; 32; 40
6. 15
7. 130 cm
8. $\frac{3}{8}$
9. $3\frac{1}{4}$; $3\frac{7}{8}$
10. Cost of printer = \$1857 ÷ 3 = **\$619**

    \$1857
    computer
    printer

11. Amount he earns in 6 months = \$1460 x 6 = **\$8760**
12. $\frac{2}{5}$
13. $\frac{2}{9}$; $\frac{2}{7}$; $\frac{2}{3}$; $\frac{9}{7}$
14. $1\frac{5}{8}$; $1\frac{3}{4}$; $2\frac{1}{8}$
15. $\frac{3}{5}$
16. $\frac{13}{5}$
17. $4\frac{3}{4}$
18. $\frac{3}{5}$ x 10 = **6**

US› 19. Total needed = $6 \times \frac{3}{5}$ yd = $\mathbf{3\frac{3}{5}}$ **yd**

3d› 19. Total needed = $6 \times \frac{3}{5}$ m = $\mathbf{3\frac{3}{5}}$ **m**

20. Number of chocolate cookies = $\frac{3}{5} \times 50$ = **30**

21. 9:45 p.m.

US› 22. Number of sticks of beef satay
= 1185 ÷ 3 = **395**

3d› 22. Number of sticks of mutton satay
= 1185 ÷ 3 = **395**

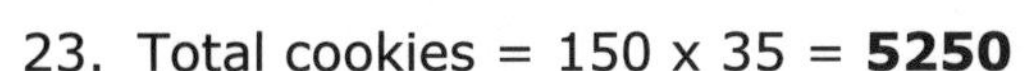

23. Total cookies = 150 x 35 = **5250**

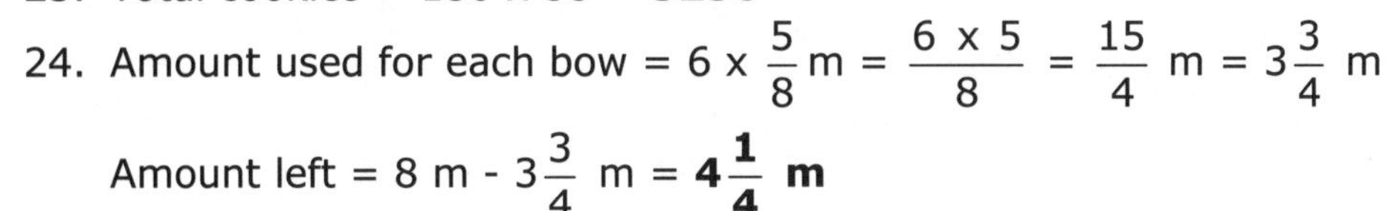

24. Amount used for each bow = $6 \times \frac{5}{8}$ m = $\frac{6 \times 5}{8} = \frac{15}{4}$ m = $3\frac{3}{4}$ m

Amount left = 8 m - $3\frac{3}{4}$ m = $\mathbf{4\frac{1}{4}}$ **m**

Exercise 36

Check bar graphs.

Exercise 37

1. Check bar graph.
2. Check bar graph.
Number sold: 440; 470; 580; 550
Total sold: 2440

Exercise 38

1. (a) Thursday (b) 39 (c) Friday
(d) Difference = 42 – 35 = **7**
(e) Total T-shirts sold = 35 + 42 + 39 + 44 + 28 = 188
Total money collected = 188 x \$8 = **\$1504**

2. (a) Fairy Tales (b) 5 (c) Fairy Tales
(d) Difference = 11 – 7 = **4**
(e) Total number of children = 5 + 6 + 7 + 11 + 12 = 41
Number of girls = 41 – 15 = **26**

Exercise 39

1 (a) Total number of boys = 22 + 15 + 22 + 21 = **80**
(b) Total number of girls = 19 + 27 + 22 + 20 = **88**
(c) **8** more **girls** than boys
(d) Total number of students = 80 + 88 = **168**

2. (a) Total spent = $3.90 x 2 = **$7.80**
(b) Difference = $7.80 - $6.70 = **$1.10**
(c) Total spent = $6.70 + $5.15 + $5.15 = **$17.00**

3. (a) Total spent = 3 x $3.20 = **$9.60**
(b) Cost of 2 small bottles = 2 x $1.80 = $3.60
Change = $20 - $3.60 = **$16.40**

US› (c) Mary spent $5.95
Emily spent 2 x $3.20 = $6.40
Amount more **Emily** spent = $6.40 - $5.95 = **$0.45**

3d› (c) Mary spent $5.95
Aihua spent 2 x $3.20 = $6.40
Amount more **Aihua** spent = $6.40 - $5.95 = **$0.45**

Exercise 40

1. (a) Total stamps collected = 220 + 200 = **420**
(b) Difference = 220 – 200 = **20**

2. (a) Total sold = 237 + 298 = **535**
(b) By observation, he sold the most pies on Saturday or Sunday.
Total pies sold Saturday = 48 + 63 = 111
Total pies sold Sunday = 65 + 50 = 115
He sold the most pies on **Sunday**.
(c) Money made from apple pies sold on Saturday = 48 x $2 = $96
Money made from chicken pies sold on Saturday = 63 x $3 = $189
Total money made Saturday = $96 + $189 = $285
Money made from apple pies sold on Sunday = 65 x $2 = $130
Money made from chicken pies sold on Sunday = 50 x $3 = $150
Total money made Sunday = $280
He made the most money on **Saturday**.
(d) Total money made from apple pies = 237 + $2 = $474
Total money made from chicken pies = 298 x $3 = $894
Total money made = $474 + $894 = **$1368**

Exercise 41

1. ∠b = 70° ∠c = 50° ∠d = 30° ∠e = 83°

2. ∠a = 100° ∠b = 120° ∠c = 140°
∠d = 160° ∠e = 110° ∠f = 130°

Exercise 42

1. $\angle a = 60°$ $\angle b = 90°$
   $\angle c = 105°$ $\angle d = 75°$
   $\angle e = 65°$ $\angle f = 120°$

2. $\angle a = 80°$ $\angle b = 125°$ $\angle c = 120°$
   $\angle d = 70°$ $\angle e = 140°$ $\angle f = 135°$

3-6. Check angles

Exercise 43

1. (b) 360° - **160° = 200°** (c) 360° - **130° = 230°**
   (d) 360° - **113° = 247°** (e) 360° - **90° = 270°**

2. (a) 360° - **60° = 300°** (b) 360° - **25° = 335°**
   (c) 360° - **65° = 295°** (d) 360° - **37° = 323°**
   (e) 360° - **32° = 328°** (f) 360° - **74° = 286°**

3. $\angle a = 60°$ $\angle b = 215°$ $\angle c = 250°$
   $\angle d = 30°$ $\angle e = 100°$ $\angle f = 290°$

Exercise 44

1. (a) $\angle CBD$ = 90° - 60° = **30°** (b) $\angle PRQ$ = 90° - 55° = **35°**
   (c) $\angle MNQ$ = 90° - 64° = **26°** (d) $\angle XYZ$ = 90° - 45° = **45°**
   (e) $\angle FEG$ = 90° - 26° = **64°** (f) $\angle JKM$ = 90° - 62° = **28°**

Exercise 45

1. not perpendicular
   not perpendicular
   perpendicular
   perpendicular
   not perpendicular

2. XY ⊥ **XZ**
   PR ⊥ **QR**
   HK ⊥ JK, JK ⊥ IJ
   AE ⊥ DE, AB ⊥ BC, BC ⊥ CD

Exercise 46

Check drawings.

Exercise 47

1. AB // **EF**
   MN // YZ
   PS // QR
   KN // LM, MN // KL

2. AB // CD, EF // GH, WZ // XY, ON // LM, LO // MN
   SR ⊥ PQ, IJ ⊥ JK, XW ⊥ XY, WZ ⊥ WX

Exercise 48

Check drawings.

Exercise 49

1. (a) CD = **5 cm**
   Area = 9 cm x 5 cm = **45 cm^2**

US› (b) Length + Width = 42 in. ÷ 2 = 21 in.
EF = 21 in. − 6 in. = **15 in.**
Area = 15 in. x 6 in. = **90 in.^{2}**

3d› (b) Length + Width = 42 cm ÷ 2 = 21 cm
EF = 21 cm − 6 cm = **15 cm**
Area = 15 cm x 6 cm = **90 cm^2**

(c) Length + Width = 26 m ÷ 2 = 13 m
SR = 13 m − 7 m = **6 m**
Area = 6 m x 7 m = **42 m^2**

2.

	Length	Width	Perimeter
A.		6 cm	28 cm
US› B.	16 ft		52 ft
3d› B.	16 m		52 m
US› C.		10 in.	40 in.
3d› C.		10 cm	40 cm
D.	15 m		48 m
US› E.	14 yd		44 yd
3d› E.	14 m		44 m

Exercise 50

(measurements are given starting from the top of the figure and moving clockwise around it.)

1. (a) Perimeter = 9 + 9 + 9 + 6 + 15 + 6 + 3 + 9 = **66 cm**
   (or: Perimeter = 2 x (18 + 15))
   (b) Perimeter = 15 + 6 + 6 + 3 + 9 + 9 = **48 m**
   (or: Perimeter = 2 x (15 + 9))
   (c) Perimeter = 8 + 6 + 10 + 5 + 10 + 6 +
   8 + 6 + 10 + 5 + 10 = **90 cm**
   (or: Perimeter = 2 x (28 + 17))
2. (a) Perimeter = 8 + 6 + 10 + 4 + 10 + 6 + 8 + 16 = **68 cm**
   (or: Perimeter = 2 x (18 + 16))
   (b) Perimeter = 5 + 5 + 10 + 10 + 25 + 5 + 10 + 10 = **80 m**
   (or: Perimeter = 2 x (25 + 15))
   (d) Perimeter = 8 + 7 + 10 + 7 + 8 + 13 + 8 + 18 + 20 = **106 m**
   (or: Perimeter = 2 x (26 + 20) + (2 x 7))

Exercise 51

Solutions will vary. The figure can be cut up into rectangles, and the areas of each added, or areas can be subtracted from a larger rectangle. Solutions which give the fewest rectangles are given here.

1. (a)

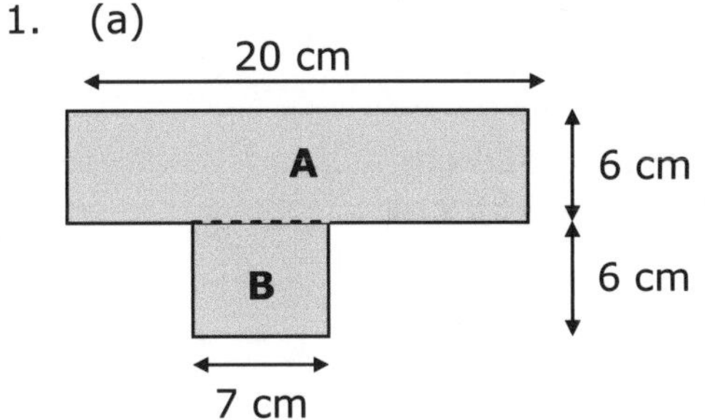

Area of A = 20 cm x 6 cm = 120 cm^2

Area of B = 7 cm x 6 cm = 42 cm^2

Total area = 120 cm + 42 cm = **162 cm^2**

(b)

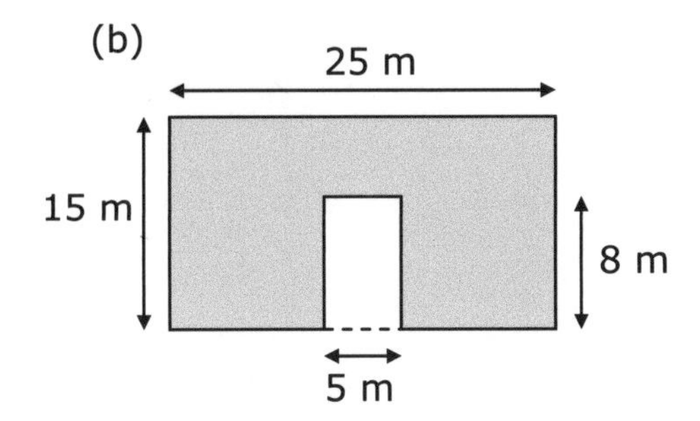

Area of large rectangle =
15 m x 25 m = 375 m^2

Area of little rectangle =
5 m x 8 m = 40 m^2

Area of shaded region =
375 m - 40 m = **335 m^2**

(c)

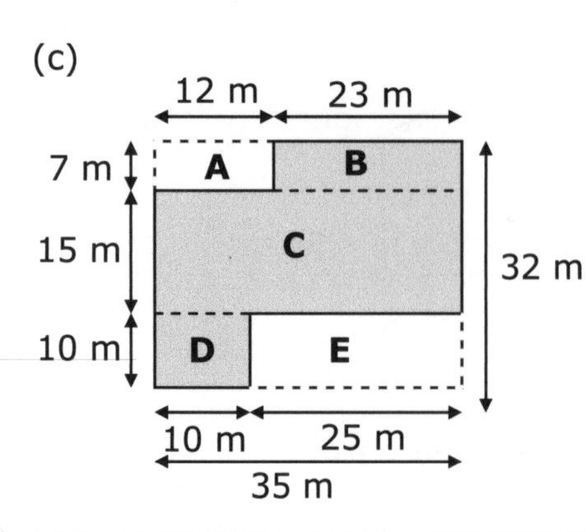

Area of large rectangle = 35 x 32 = 1120 m^2
Area of A = 12 x 7 = 84 m^2
Area of E = 25 x 10 = 250 m^2
Area shaded region = 1120 – 84 – 250 = **786 m^2**
or
Area of B = 7 x 23 = 161 m^2
Area of C = 15 x 35 = 525 m^2
Area of D = 10 x 10 = 100 m^2
Area of shaded region = 161 + 525 + 100 = 786 m^2

Exercise 52

1. (a) Area of large rectangle = 16 m x 8 m = 128 m^2
   Area of small rectangle = 12 m x 4 m = 48 m^2
   Area of shaded part = 128 m^2 – 48 m^2 = **80 m^2**
   (b) Area of large rectangle = 9 m x 5 m = 45 m^2
   Area of small rectangle = 3 m x 3 m = 9 m^2
   Area of shaded part = 45 m^2 – 9 m^2 = **36 m^2**
   (d) Area of large rectangle = 20 cm x 16 cm = 320 cm^2
   Area of small rectangle = 5 cm x 8 cm = 40 cm^2
   Area of shaded part = 320 cm^2 – 40 cm^2 = **280 cm^2**

2. Area of pool + path = 22 m x 14 m = 308 m^2
   Area of pool = 20 m x 12 m = 240 m^2
   Area of path = 308 m^2 – 240 m^2 = **68 m^2**

3. Area of towel = 60 cm x 96 cm = 5760 cm^2
   Area without border = 54 cm x 90 cm = 4860 cm^2
   Area of border = 5760 cm^2 – 4860 cm^2 = **900 cm^2**

Review 4

1. (a) \$5703 (b) \$34,864
2. hundred
3. 100
4. $\frac{23}{5}$
5. 750 ml or $\frac{3}{4}$ liters
6. Perimeter = 6 cm x 4 = **24 cm**
7. Area of each square is 4 cm^2. There are 16 squares.
   Total area = 4 cm^2 x 16 = **64 cm^2**

US› 8. (a) Mary (b) Dani
3d› 8. (a) Mary (b) Devi

9. (a) 146°, 34° (b) 303°, 57°

10. (a) PQ (b) CD

11. (a) Thursday (b) 630

12. 8 cm

13. 28 m

US› 14. Length of shorter piece
= 1080 in. ÷ 3 = **360 in.**
3d› 14. Length of shorter piece
= 1080 cm ÷ 3 = **360 cm**

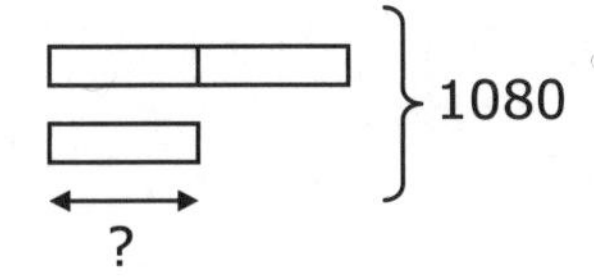

15. 216 m

16. Area of rectangle = 9 cm x 4 cm = 36 cm^2 = Area of square.
6 x 6 = 36. Length of side of square = **6 cm**

17. Area of room = 8 m x 6 m = 48 m^2
Area of carpet = 6 m x 4 m = 24 m^2
Area of room not covered = 48 m^2 - 24 m^2 = **24 m^2**

Mental Math 1			
1.	43	16.	131
2.	64	17.	176
3.	78	18.	77
4.	100	19.	145
5.	146	20.	126
6.	102	21.	119
7.	172	22.	133
8.	103	23.	66
9.	125	24.	161
10.	131	25.	374
11.	155	26.	103
12.	127	27.	888
13.	145	28.	200
14.	103	29.	260
15.	101	30.	206

Mental Math 2			
1.	59	16.	123
2.	29	17.	56
3.	44	18.	23
4.	32	19.	72
5.	21	20.	44
6.	57	21.	192
7.	18	22.	258
8.	14	23.	419
9.	34	24.	967
10.	26	25.	713
11.	16	26.	547
12.	53	27.	34
13.	7	28.	57
14.	32	29.	25
15.	15	30.	103

Mental Math 3			
1.	1700	16.	34,480
2.	26,000	17.	44,000
3.	92,000	18.	49,320
4.	51,000	19.	26,110
5.	40,000	20.	45,450
6.	71,000	21.	34,100
7.	8300	22.	3700
8.	95,000	23.	11,700
9.	91,000	24.	40,100
10.	75,000	25.	90,000
11.	7560	26.	86,100
12.	30,000	27.	87,639
13.	4670	28.	84,778
14.	30,000	29.	80,000
15.	14,200	30.	33,500

Mental Math 4			
1.	42,000	16.	88,500
2.	36,000	17.	23,500
3.	12,000	18.	23,300
4.	67,000	19.	68,700
5.	77,000	20.	26,100
6.	43,000	21.	37,000
7.	9999	22.	65,001
8.	14,000	23.	32,600
9.	79,000	24.	61,000
10.	45,000	25.	91,800
11.	46,000	26.	60,910
12.	45,000	27.	52,996
13.	22,000	28.	85,431
14.	12,600	29.	51,436
15.	55,300	30.	89,731

Mental Math 5			
1.	2500	16.	64,000
2.	54,000	17.	30,000
3.	35,000	18.	2400
4.	56,000	19.	72,000
5.	48,000	20.	4900
6.	8100	21.	40,000
7.	36,000	22.	42,000
8.	60,000	23.	63,000
9.	32,000	24.	24,000
10.	80,000	25.	18,000
11.	2100	26.	28,000
12.	90,000	27.	3600
13.	27,000	28.	16,000
14.	10,000	29.	40,000
15.	1200	30.	16,000

Mental Math 6			
1.	8000	16.	8000
2.	2000	17.	70
3.	7000	18.	300
4.	7000	19.	4000
5.	600	20.	9000
6.	9000	21.	4000
7.	600	22.	6000
8.	4000	23.	600
9.	50	24.	5000
10.	6000	25.	500
11.	7000	26.	9000
12.	30,000	27.	500
13.	3000	28.	300
14.	5000	29.	3000
15.	2000	30.	4000

Mental Math 7			
1.	7200	16.	12,000
2.	120	17.	4200
3.	600	18.	11,700
4.	560	19.	5000
5.	42	20.	180
6.	81	21.	27,000
7.	480	22.	14,600
8.	24	23.	6200
9.	45	24.	6000
10.	36	25.	800
11.	280	26.	91
12.	90	27.	500
13.	2400	28.	25,300
14.	250	29.	14,950
15.	1000	30.	16,200

Mental Math 8			
1.	2500	16.	64,000
2.	54,000	17.	3000
3.	35,000	18.	24,000
4.	56,000	19.	7200
5.	4800	20.	49,000
6.	81,000	21.	4000
7.	36,000	22.	42,000
8.	90,000	23.	6300
9.	32,000	24.	24,000
10.	4500	25.	18,000
11.	2100	26.	2800
12.	80,000	27.	3600
13.	27,000	28.	16,000
14.	10,000	29.	8000
15.	1200	30.	16,000

Mental Math 9			
1.	265	16.	6480
2.	558	17.	3036
3.	399	18.	2460
4.	568	19.	7290
5.	498	20.	1464
6.	828	21.	4080
7.	372	22.	4214
8.	84	23.	2763
9.	360	24.	2766
10.	116	25.	1864
11.	252	26.	9604
12.	1110	27.	2468
13.	3420	28.	16,868
14.	3350	29.	14,810
15.	1560	30.	20,992

Mental Math 10			
1.	12	16.	520
2.	29	17.	128
3.	14	18.	111
4.	25	19.	131
5.	33	20.	514
6.	22	21.	220
7.	48	22.	210
8.	17	23.	625
9.	50	24.	180
10.	141	25.	436
11.	28	26.	3301
12.	181	27.	6010
13.	59	28.	1500
14.	71	29.	3197
15.	21	30.	4006

Mental Math 11			
1.	295	16.	2100
2.	621	17.	1400
3.	399	18.	20,500
4.	632	19.	20,300
5.	534	20.	18,300
6.	9108	21.	4045
7.	414	22.	4263
8.	928	23.	4900
9.	392	24.	2814
10.	4158	25.	2475
11.	273	26.	1196
12.	7164	27.	2598
13.	261	28.	10,600
14.	10348	29.	15,249
15.	156	30.	6700

Mental Math 12			
1.	146	16.	54,000
2.	117	17.	5530
3.	196	18.	1752
4.	552	19.	1518
5.	13,000	20.	1501
6.	56,000	21.	5383
7.	51,400	22.	4893
8.	89,877	23.	23,300
9.	80,000	24.	15,875
10.	64,000	25.	8562
11.	7000	26.	1596
12.	6000	27.	12,598
13.	361	28.	8700
14.	10,700	29.	7477
15.	294	30.	20,600

Mental Math 13			
1.	$\frac{3}{4}$	14.	$\frac{8}{9}$
2.	$\frac{5}{8}$	15.	$\frac{5}{8}$
3.	$\frac{7}{8}$	16.	$\frac{7}{15}$
4.	$\frac{13}{100}$	17.	$\frac{13}{16}$
5.	$\frac{4}{9}$	18.	$\frac{83}{100}$
6.	$\frac{3}{8}$	19.	$\frac{7}{9}$
7.	$\frac{9}{10}$	20.	$\frac{1}{2}$
8.	$\frac{5}{9}$	21.	$\frac{5}{6}$
9.	$\frac{11}{16}$	22.	$\frac{1}{2}$
10.	$\frac{7}{10}$	23.	$\frac{3}{4}$
11.	$\frac{5}{8}$	24.	$\frac{5}{6}$
12.	$\frac{8}{9}$	25.	$\frac{2}{3}$
13.	$\frac{7}{12}$	26.	$\frac{1}{4}$

Mental Math 14			
1.	$\frac{1}{4}$	14.	$\frac{5}{9}$
2.	$\frac{1}{6}$	15.	$\frac{5}{8}$
3.	$\frac{3}{8}$	16.	$\frac{3}{10}$
4.	$\frac{1}{4}$	17.	$\frac{1}{8}$
5.	$\frac{1}{10}$	18.	$\frac{4}{9}$
6.	$\frac{3}{8}$	19.	$\frac{2}{9}$
7.	$\frac{7}{100}$	20.	$\frac{29}{100}$
8.	$\frac{2}{9}$	21.	$\frac{1}{2}$
9.	$\frac{1}{8}$	22.	$\frac{1}{2}$
10.	$\frac{1}{9}$	23.	$\frac{2}{3}$
11.	$\frac{1}{8}$	24.	$\frac{1}{6}$
12.	$\frac{3}{10}$	25.	$\frac{1}{4}$
13.	$\frac{1}{8}$	26.	$\frac{1}{3}$

Mental Math 15			
1.	$2\frac{3}{4}$	14.	$2\frac{2}{3}$
2.	$5\frac{5}{6}$	15.	$8\frac{1}{4}$
3.	$9\frac{7}{8}$	16.	$4\frac{3}{5}$
4.	$11\frac{1}{2}$	17.	$\frac{2}{5}$
5.	$7\frac{4}{5}$	18.	$6\frac{9}{10}$
6.	$2\frac{1}{4}$	19.	$\frac{5}{9}$
7.	$4\frac{7}{10}$	20.	$4\frac{11}{100}$
8.	$9\frac{19}{20}$	21.	$\frac{5}{6}$
9.	$7\frac{13}{20}$	22.	$3\frac{5}{6}$
10.	$4\frac{91}{100}$	23.	$1\frac{5}{6}$
11.	$3\frac{7}{8}$	24.	$2\frac{1}{5}$
12.	$1\frac{4}{5}$	25.	$4\frac{5}{9}$
13.	$1\frac{3}{4}$	26.	$1\frac{1}{6}$

Mental Math 16			
1.	$1\frac{1}{3}$	14.	$1\frac{11}{16}$
2.	$1\frac{1}{4}$	15.	$1\frac{1}{3}$
3.	$1\frac{1}{6}$	16.	$1\frac{1}{3}$
4.	$1\frac{1}{2}$	17.	$1\frac{5}{16}$
5.	$1\frac{1}{4}$	18.	$1\frac{61}{100}$
6.	$1\frac{3}{8}$	19.	$1\frac{1}{21}$
7.	$1\frac{1}{2}$	20.	$1\frac{1}{2}$
8.	$1\frac{2}{9}$	21.	$1\frac{1}{3}$
9.	$1\frac{5}{16}$	22.	$1\frac{13}{20}$
10.	$1\frac{1}{5}$	23.	$1\frac{7}{100}$
11.	$1\frac{1}{8}$	24.	$1\frac{7}{16}$
12.	$1\frac{4}{9}$	25.	$1\frac{11}{25}$
13.	$1\frac{1}{4}$	26.	$1\frac{9}{20}$

Mental Math 17			
1.	12	14.	8
2.	2	15.	25
3.	10	16.	8
4.	21	17.	6
5.	12	18.	130
6.	24	19.	36
7.	20	20.	15
8.	10	21.	9
9.	7	22.	40
10.	18	23.	25
11.	21	24.	75
12.	20	25.	40
13.	10	26.	50

Mental Math 18			
1.	$3\frac{1}{8}$	16.	$6\frac{3}{4}$
2.	$3\frac{1}{5}$	17.	36
3.	$2\frac{2}{5}$	18.	$16\frac{1}{4}$
4.	$1\frac{1}{3}$	19.	$8\frac{2}{5}$
5.	$2\frac{2}{5}$	20.	$14\frac{2}{3}$
6.	$1\frac{1}{3}$	21.	$10\frac{5}{8}$
7.	$2\frac{1}{4}$	22.	$5\frac{2}{5}$
8.	3	23.	$6\frac{4}{9}$
9.	7	24.	22
10.	$4\frac{4}{5}$	25.	$1\frac{1}{6}$
11.	$15\frac{5}{7}$	26.	$1\frac{1}{2}$
12.	$8\frac{1}{2}$	27.	$4\frac{1}{2}$
13.	$6\frac{1}{2}$	28.	$2\frac{2}{3}$

Blank page

Mental Math 1

1. 37 + 6 = ________
2. 38 + 26 = ________
3. 69 + 9 = ________
4. 46 + 54 = ________
5. 96 + 50 = ________
6. 16 + 86 = ________
7. 92 + 80 = ________
8. 34 + 69 = ________
9. 91 + 34 = ________
10. 65 + 66 = ________
11. 62 + 93 = ________
12. 81 + 46 = ________
13. 65 + 80 = ________
14. 81 + 22 = ________
15. 32 + 69 = ________
16. 41 + 90 = ________
17. 78 + 98 = ________
18. 49 + 28 = ________
19. 48 + 97 = ________
20. 27 + 99 = ________
21. 38 + 81 = ________
22. 99 + 34 = ________
23. 39 + 27 = ________
24. 116 + 45 = ________
25. 325 + 49 = ________
26. 48 + 55 = ________
27. 789 + 99 = ________
28. 126 + 74 = ________
29. 227 + 33 = ________
30. 119 + 87 = ________

Mental Math 2

1. 98 – 39 = ________
2. 84 – 55 = ________
3. 73 – 29 = ________
4. 50 – 18 = ________
5. 93 – 72 = ________
6. 66 – 9 = ________
7. 53 – 35 = ________
8. 60 – 46 = ________
9. 72 – 38 = ________
10. 55 – 29 = ________
11. 60 – 44 = ________
12. 92 – 39 = ________
13. 22 – 15 = ________
14. 88 – 56 = ________
15. 32 – 17 = ________
16. 183 – 60 = ________
17. 136 – 80 = ________
18. 100 – 77 = ________
19. 100 – 28 = ________
20. 143 – 99 = ________
21. 290 – 98 = ________
22. 300 – 42 = ________
23. 500 – 81 = ________
24. 995 – 28 = ________
25. 748 – 35 = ________
26. 644 – 97 = ________
27. 132 – 98 = ________
28. 156 – 99 = ________
29. 120 – 95 = ________
30. 199 – 96 = ________

Mental Math 3

1. 1400 + 300 = ________
2. 17,000 + 9000 = ________
3. 89,000 + 3000 = ________
4. 46,000 + 5000 = ________
5. 32,000 + 8000 = ________
6. 45,000 + 26,000 = ________
7. 2300 + 6000 = ________
8. 45,000 + 50,000 = ________
9. 28,000 + 63,000 = ________
10. 32,000 + 43,000 = ________
11. 4560 + 3000 = ________
12. 24,000 + 6000 = ________
13. 4580 + 90 = ________
14. 23,000 + 7000 = ________
15. 9200 + 5000 = ________
16. 3480 + 31,000 = ________
17. 25,000 + 19,000 = ________
18. 8320 + 41,000 = ________
19. 25,800 + 310 = ________
20. 45,300 + 150 = ________
21. 27,000+ 7100 = ________
22. 500 + 3200 = ________
23. 6000 + 5700 = ________
24. 40,001 + 99 = ________
25. 89,001 + 999 = ________
26. 400 + 85,700 = ________
27. 45,123 + 42,516 = ________
28. 81,562 + 3216 = ________
29. 79,999 + 1 = ________
30. 90 + 33,410 = ________

Mental Math 4

1. 51,000 – 9,000 = _______
2. 42,000 – 6000 = _______
3. 38,000 – 26,000 = _______
4. 84,000 – 17,000 = _______
5. 82,000 – 5000 = _______
6. 49,000 – 6000 = _______
7. 10,000 – 1 = _______
8. 23,000 – 9000 = _______
9. 82,000 – 3000 = _______
10. 51,000 – 6000 = _______
11. 92,000 – 46,000 = _______
12. 54,000 – 9,000 = _______
13. 59,000 – 37,000 = _______
14. 13,400 – 800 = _______
15. 62,300 – 7000 = _______
16. 89,200 – 700 = _______
17. 24,000 – 500 = _______
18. 24,100 – 800 = _______
19. 69,300 – 600 = _______
20. 35,100 – 9000 = _______
21. 41,000 – 4000 = _______
22. 65,100 – 99 = _______
23. 33,400 – 800 = _______
24. 91,000 – 30,000 = _______
25. 92,000 – 200 = _______
26. 61,000 – 90 = _______
27. 53,000 – 4 = _______
28. 89,583 – 4152 = _______
29. 59,598 – 8162 = _______
30. 89,962 – 231 = _______

Mental Math 5

1. $500 \times 5 =$ ________
2. $6000 \times 9 =$ ________
3. $5000 \times 7 =$ ________
4. $7000 \times 8 =$ ________
5. $8000 \times 6 =$ ________
6. $9 \times 900 =$ ________
7. $6000 \times 6 =$ ________
8. $20{,}000 \times 3 =$ ________
9. $4000 \times 8 =$ ________
10. $20{,}000 \times 4 =$ ________
11. $300 \times 7 =$ ________
12. $3 \times 30{,}000 =$ ________
13. $3000 \times 9 =$ ________
14. $2 \times 5000 =$ ________
15. $300 \times 4 =$ ________
16. $8000 \times 8 =$ ________
17. $5 \times 6000 =$ ________
18. $800 \times 3 =$ ________
19. $8000 \times 9 =$ ________
20. $7 \times 700 =$ ________
21. $8000 \times 5 =$ ________
22. $6000 \times 7 =$ ________
23. $9 \times 7000 =$ ________
24. $4000 \times 6 =$ ________
25. $9000 \times 2 =$ ________
26. $7000 \times 4 =$ ________
27. $4 \times 900 =$ ________
28. $4000 \times 4 =$ ________
29. $2 \times 20{,}000 =$ ________
30. $2000 \times 8 =$ ________

Mental Math 6

1. 72,000 ÷ 9 = ________
2. 12,000 ÷ 6 = ________
3. 63,000 ÷ 9 = ________
4. 56,000 ÷ 8 = ________
5. 4200 ÷ 7 = ________
6. 81,000 ÷ 9 = ________
7. 4800 ÷ 8 = ________
8. 24,000 ÷ 6 = ________
9. 450 ÷ 9 = ________
10. 36,000 ÷ 6 = ________
11. 28,000 ÷ 4 = ________
12. 90,000 ÷ 3 = ________
13. 24,000 ÷ 8 = ________
14. 25,000 ÷ 5 = ________
15. 10,000 ÷ 5 = ________
16. 24,000 ÷ 3 = ________
17. 490 ÷ 7 = ________
18. 2700 ÷ 9 = ________
19. 32,000 ÷ 8 = ________
20. 18,000 ÷ 2 = ________
21. 20,000 ÷ 5 = ________
22. 54,000 ÷ 9 = ________
23. 1800 ÷ 3 = ________
24. 40,000 ÷ 8 = ________
25. 3500 ÷ 7 = ________
26. 36,000 ÷ 4 = ________
27. 3000 ÷ 6 = ________
28. 2100 ÷ 7 = ________
29. 15,000 ÷ 5 = ________
30. 16,000 ÷ 4 = ________

Mental Math 7

1. 72,000 ÷ 10 = ________
2. 12,000 ÷ 100 = ________
3. 6000 ÷ 10 = ________
4. 5600 ÷ 10 = ________
5. 4200 ÷ 100 = ________
6. 81,000 ÷ 1000 = ________
7. 4800 ÷ 10 = ________
8. 2400 ÷ 100 = ________
9. 450 ÷ 10 = ________
10. 36,000 ÷ 1000 = ________
11. 2800 ÷ 10 = ________
12. 90,000 ÷ 1000 = ________
13. 24,000 ÷ 10 = ________
14. 25,000 ÷ 100 = ________
15. 10,000 ÷ 10 = ________
16. 4,000 x 3 = ________
17. 4900 – 700 = ________
18. 2700 + 9000 = ________
19. 40,000 ÷ 8 = ________
20. 18,000 ÷ 100 = ________
21. 32,000 – 5000 = ________
22. 5400 + 9200 = ________
23. 9800 – 3600 = ________
24. 42,000 ÷ 7 = ________
25. 5600 ÷ 7 = ________
26. 91,000 ÷ 1000 = ________
27. 3000 ÷ 6 = ________
28. 26,000 – 700 = ________
29. 15,000 – 50 = ________
30. 16,000 + 200 = ________

Mental Math 8

1. 50 x 50 = _________
2. 600 x 90 = _________
3. 500 x 70 = _________
4. 7000 x 8 = _________
5. 80 x 60 = _________
6. 90 x 900 = _________
7. 600 x 60 = _________
8. 300 x 300 = _________
9. 400 x 80 = _________
10. 9 x 500 = _________
11. 300 x 7 = _________
12. 200 x 400 = _________
13. 300 x 90 = _________
14. 20 x 500 = _________
15. 30 x 40 = _________
16. 800 x 80 = _________
17. 50 x 60 = _________
18. 800 x 30 = _________
19. 80 x 90 = _________
20. 70 x 700 = _________
21. 80 x 50 = _________
22. 600 x 70 = _________
23. 90 x 70 = _________
24. 400 x 60 = _________
25. 900 x 20 = _________
26. 70 x 40 = _________
27. 40 x 90 = _________
28. 400 x 40 = _________
29. 40 x 200 = _________
30. 20 x 800 = _________

Mental Math 9

1. 53 x 5 = ________
2. 62 x 9 = ________
3. 57 x 7 = ________
4. 71 x 8 = ________
5. 83 x 6 = ________
6. 9 x 92 = ________
7. 62 x 6 = ________
8. 28 x 3 = ________
9. 45 x 8 = ________
10. 29 x 4 = ________
11. 36 x 7 = ________
12. 370 x 3 = ________
13. 380 x 9 = ________
14. 670 x 5 = ________
15. 390 x 4 = ________
16. 810 x 8 = ________
17. 506 x 6 = ________
18. 820 x 3 = ________
19. 810 x 9 = ________
20. 732 x 2 = ________
21. 816 x 5 = ________
22. 602 x 7 = ________
23. 921 x 3 = ________
24. 461 x 6 = ________
25. 932 x 2 = ________
26. 2401 x 4 = ________
27. 1234 x 2 = ________
28. 4217 x 4 = ________
29. 2962 x 5 = ________
30. 2624 x 8 = ________

Mental Math 10

1. $108 \div 9 =$ ________
2. $174 \div 6 =$ ________
3. $126 \div 9 =$ ________
4. $200 \div 8 =$ ________
5. $231 \div 7 =$ ________
6. $198 \div 9 =$ ________
7. $240 \div 5 =$ ________
8. $102 \div 6 =$ ________
9. $450 \div 9 =$ ________
10. $846 \div 6 =$ ________
11. $112 \div 4 =$ ________
12. $543 \div 3 =$ ________
13. $472 \div 8 =$ ________
14. $355 \div 5 =$ ________
15. $105 \div 5 =$ ________
16. $1560 \div 3 =$ ________
17. $896 \div 7 =$ ________
18. $999 \div 9 =$ ________
19. $1048 \div 8 =$ ________
20. $1028 \div 2 =$ ________
21. $1100 \div 5 =$ ________
22. $1890 \div 9 =$ ________
23. $1875 \div 3 =$ ________
24. $1440 \div 8 =$ ________
25. $3052 \div 7 =$ ________
26. $13{,}204 \div 4 =$ ________
27. $36{,}060 \div 6 =$ ________
28. $10{,}500 \div 7 =$ ________
29. $15{,}985 \div 5 =$ ________
30. $16{,}024 \div 4 =$ ________

Mental Math 11

1. 59 x 5 = ________
2. 69 x 9 = ________
3. 57 x 7 = ________
4. 79 x 8 = ________
5. 89 x 6 = ________
6. 99 x 92 = ________
7. 69 x 6 = ________
8. 29 x 32 = ________
9. 49 x 8 = ________
10. 99 x 42 = ________
11. 39 x 7 = ________
12. 199 x 36 = ________
13. 29 x 9 = ________
14. 199 x 52 = ________
15. 39 x 4 = ________
16. 84 x 25 = ________
17. 56 x 25 = ________
18. 820 x 25 = ________
19. 812 x 25 = ________
20. 732 x 25 = ________
21. 809 x 5 = ________
22. 609 x 7 = ________
23. 196 x 25 = ________
24. 469 x 6 = ________
25. 99 x 25 = ________
26. 299 x 4 = ________
27. 1299 x 2 = ________
28. 424 x 25 = ________
29. 299 x 51 = ________
30. 268 x 25 = ________

Mental Math 12

1. $47 + 99 =$ ________
2. $36 + 81 =$ ________
3. $294 - 98 =$ ________
4. $600 - 48 =$ ________
5. $9400 + 3600 =$ ________
6. $47{,}000 + 9000 =$ ________
7. $59{,}500 - 8100 =$ ________
8. $89{,}900 - 23 =$ ________
9. $2 \times 40{,}000 =$ ________
10. $8000 \times 8 =$ ________
11. $35{,}000 \div 5 =$ ________
12. $54{,}000 \div 9 =$ ________
13. $36{,}100 \div 100 =$ ________
14. $3800 + 6900 =$ ________
15. $49 \times 6 =$ ________
16. $600 \times 90 =$ ________
17. $79 \times 70 =$ ________
18. $219 \times 8 =$ ________
19. $506 \times 3 =$ ________
20. $10507 \div 7 =$ ________
21. $26{,}915 \div 5 =$ ________
22. $699 \times 7 =$ ________
23. $932 \times 25 =$ ________
24. $15{,}925 - 50 =$ ________
25. $34{,}248 \div 4 =$ ________
26. $399 \times 4 =$ ________
27. $6299 \times 2 =$ ________
28. $348 \times 25 =$ ________
29. $29908 \div 4 =$ ________
30. $824 \times 25 =$ ________

Mental Math 13

1. $\frac{1}{2} + \frac{1}{4} = \_\_\_$

2. $\frac{1}{8} + \frac{1}{2} = \_\_\_$

3. $\frac{1}{4} + \frac{5}{8} = \_\_\_$

4. $\frac{1}{10} + \frac{3}{100} = \_\_\_$

5. $\frac{1}{3} + \frac{1}{9} = \_\_\_$

6. $\frac{1}{4} + \frac{1}{8} = \_\_\_$

7. $\frac{1}{5} + \frac{7}{10} = \_\_\_$

8. $\frac{1}{3} + \frac{2}{9} = \_\_\_$

9. $\frac{1}{16} + \frac{5}{8} = \_\_\_$

10. $\frac{3}{10} + \frac{2}{5} = \_\_\_$

11. $\frac{1}{4} + \frac{3}{8} = \_\_\_$

12. $\frac{2}{3} + \frac{2}{9} = \_\_\_$

13. $\frac{5}{12} + \frac{1}{6} = \_\_\_$

14. $\frac{1}{3} + \frac{5}{9} = \_\_\_$

15. $\frac{1}{4} + \frac{3}{8} = \_\_\_$

16. $\frac{1}{15} + \frac{2}{5} = \_\_\_$

17. $\frac{3}{16} + \frac{5}{8} = \_\_\_$

18. $\frac{13}{100} + \frac{7}{10} = \_\_\_$

19. $\frac{1}{3} + \frac{4}{9} = \_\_\_$

20. $\frac{1}{3} + \frac{1}{6} = \_\_\_$

21. $\frac{1}{12} + \frac{3}{4} = \_\_\_$

22. $\frac{1}{5} + \frac{3}{10} = \_\_\_$

23. $\frac{1}{3} + \frac{5}{12} = \_\_\_$

24. $\frac{3}{4} + \frac{1}{12} = \_\_\_$

25. $\frac{5}{12} + \frac{1}{4} = \_\_\_$

26. $\frac{1}{10} + \frac{3}{20} = \_\_\_$

Mental Math 14

1. $\frac{1}{2} - \frac{1}{4} =$ ___
2. $\frac{1}{3} - \frac{1}{6} =$ ___
3. $\frac{1}{2} - \frac{1}{8} =$ ___
4. $\frac{3}{4} - \frac{1}{2} =$ ___
5. $\frac{3}{10} - \frac{1}{5} =$ ___
6. $\frac{5}{8} - \frac{1}{4} =$ ___
7. $\frac{1}{10} - \frac{3}{100} =$ ___
8. $\frac{1}{3} - \frac{1}{9} =$ ___
9. $\frac{1}{4} - \frac{1}{8} =$ ___
10. $\frac{1}{3} - \frac{2}{9} =$ ___
11. $\frac{3}{4} - \frac{5}{8} =$ ___
12. $\frac{7}{10} - \frac{2}{5} =$ ___
13. $\frac{3}{8} - \frac{1}{4} =$ ___
14. $\frac{8}{9} - \frac{1}{3} =$ ___
15. $\frac{7}{8} - \frac{1}{4} =$ ___
16. $\frac{7}{10} - \frac{2}{5} =$ ___
17. $\frac{7}{8} - \frac{3}{4} =$ ___
18. $\frac{7}{9} - \frac{1}{3} =$ ___
19. $\frac{2}{3} - \frac{4}{9} =$ ___
20. $\frac{3}{10} - \frac{1}{100} =$ ___
21. $\frac{5}{6} - \frac{1}{3} =$ ___
22. $\frac{7}{10} - \frac{1}{5} =$ ___
23. $\frac{3}{4} - \frac{1}{12} =$ ___
24. $\frac{5}{12} - \frac{1}{4} =$ ___
25. $\frac{5}{12} - \frac{1}{6} =$ ___
26. $\frac{6}{9} - \frac{1}{3} =$ ___

Mental Math 15

1. $3-\frac{1}{4}=$

2. $6-\frac{1}{6}=$

3. $10-\frac{1}{8}=$

4. $12-\frac{1}{2}=$

5. $8-\frac{1}{5}=$

6. $3-\frac{3}{4}=$

7. $5-\frac{3}{10}=$

8. $10-\frac{1}{20}=$

9. $8-\frac{7}{20}=$

10. $5-\frac{9}{100}=$

11. $5-1\frac{1}{8}=$

12. $4-2\frac{1}{5}=$

13. $3-1\frac{1}{4}=$

14. $6-3\frac{1}{3}=$

15. $10-1\frac{3}{4}=$

16. $7-2\frac{2}{5}=$

17. $5-4\frac{3}{5}=$

18. $10-3\frac{1}{10}=$

19. $12-11\frac{4}{9}=$

20. $15-10\frac{89}{100}=$

21. $\frac{1}{6}+\qquad=1$

22. $\frac{1}{6}+\qquad=4$

23. $2\frac{1}{6}+\qquad=4$

24. $7\frac{4}{5}+\qquad=10$

25. $3\frac{4}{9}+\qquad=8$

26. $\qquad+5\frac{5}{6}=7$

Mental Math 16

1. $\frac{5}{6}+\frac{3}{6}=$

2. $\frac{5}{8}+\frac{5}{8}=$

3. $\frac{7}{12}+\frac{7}{12}=$

4. $\frac{9}{10}+\frac{3}{5}=$

5. $\frac{1}{2}+\frac{3}{4}=$

6. $\frac{3}{4}+\frac{5}{8}=$

7. $\frac{4}{5}+\frac{7}{10}=$

8. $\frac{2}{3}+\frac{5}{9}=$

9. $\frac{11}{16}+\frac{5}{8}=$

10. $\frac{7}{10}+\frac{1}{2}=$

11. $\frac{1}{4}+\frac{7}{8}=$

12. $\frac{2}{3}+\frac{7}{9}=$

13. $\frac{5}{12}+\frac{5}{6}=$

14. $\frac{3}{4}+\frac{15}{16}=$

15. $\frac{23}{24}+\frac{3}{8}=$

16. $\frac{11}{15}+\frac{3}{5}=$

17. $\frac{7}{16}+\frac{7}{8}=$

18. $\frac{91}{100}+\frac{7}{10}=$

19. $\frac{10}{21}+\frac{4}{7}=$

20. $\frac{2}{3}+\frac{5}{6}=$

21. $\frac{7}{12}+\frac{3}{4}=$

22. $\frac{4}{5}+\frac{17}{20}=$

23. $\frac{1}{10}+\frac{97}{100}=$

24. $\frac{3}{4}+\frac{11}{16}=$

25. $\frac{21}{25}+\frac{3}{5}=$ ___

26. $\frac{9}{10}+\frac{11}{20}=$ ___

Mental Math 17

1. $\frac{1}{2}$ x 24 =
2. $\frac{1}{8}$ x 16 =
3. $\frac{1}{4}$ x 40 =
4. $\frac{7}{10}$ x 30 =
5. $\frac{2}{3}$ x 18 =
6. $\frac{3}{4}$ x 32 =
7. $\frac{4}{5}$ x 25 =
8. $\frac{5}{7}$ x 14 =
9. $\frac{7}{16}$ x 16 =
10. $\frac{3}{11}$ x 66 =
11. $\frac{3}{8}$ x 56 =
12. $\frac{2}{3}$ x 30 =
13. $\frac{5}{12}$ x 24 =
14. $\frac{4}{15}$ x 30 =
15. $\frac{5}{8}$ x 40 =
16. $\frac{2}{9}$ x 36 =
17. $\frac{3}{16}$ x 32 =
18. $\frac{13}{100}$ x 1000 =
19. $\frac{4}{9}$ x 81 =
20. $\frac{5}{6}$ x 18 =
21. $\frac{3}{4}$ x 12 =
22. $\frac{2}{5}$ x 100 =
23. $\frac{1}{3}$ x 75 =
24. $\frac{3}{4}$ x 100 =
25. $\frac{2}{5}$ x 100 =
26. $\frac{2}{3}$ x 75 =

Mental Math 18

1. $5 \times \frac{5}{8} =$
2. $8 \times \frac{2}{5} =$
3. $4 \times \frac{3}{5} =$
4. $\frac{2}{9} \times 6 =$
5. $\frac{4}{5} \times 3 =$
6. $\frac{2}{3} \times 2 =$
7. $\frac{3}{4} \times 3 =$
8. $2 \times 1\frac{1}{2} =$
9. $3 \times 2\frac{1}{3} =$
10. $4 \times 1\frac{1}{5} =$
11. $5 \times 3\frac{1}{7} =$
12. $2 \times 4\frac{1}{4} =$
13. $3 \times 2\frac{1}{6} =$
14. $3 \times 2\frac{1}{4} =$
15. $8 \times 4\frac{1}{2} =$
16. $5 \times 3\frac{1}{4} =$
17. $4 \times 2\frac{1}{10} =$
18. $4 \times 3\frac{2}{3} =$
19. $5 \times 2\frac{1}{8} =$
20. $2 \times 2\frac{7}{10} =$
21. $2 \times 3\frac{2}{9} =$
22. $20 \times 1\frac{1}{10} =$
23. $\frac{1}{6} \times 7 =$
24. $\frac{1}{6} \times 9 =$
25. $\frac{3}{6} \times 9 =$
26. $\frac{2}{3} \times 4 =$

1	10000
2	20000
3	30000
4	40000
5	50000
6	60000

7	70000
8	80000
9	90000
10	1000
20	2000
30	3000

4 0	4 0 0 0
5 0	5 0 0 0
6 0	6 0 0 0
7 0	7 0 0 0
8 0	8 0 0 0
9 0	9 0 0 0

1 0 0	2 0 0
3 0 0	4 0 0
5 0 0	6 0 0
7 0 0	8 0 0
9 0 0	0 0 0

0	0 0	0 0 0 0

1	2	3	4	5	6	7	8	9	10
11	12	13	14	15	16	17	18	19	20
21	22	23	24	25	26	27	28	29	30
31	32	33	34	35	36	37	38	39	40
41	42	43	44	45	46	47	48	49	50
51	52	53	54	55	56	57	58	59	60
61	62	63	64	65	66	67	68	69	70
71	72	73	74	75	76	77	78	79	80
81	82	83	84	85	86	87	88	89	90
91	92	93	94	95	96	97	98	99	100

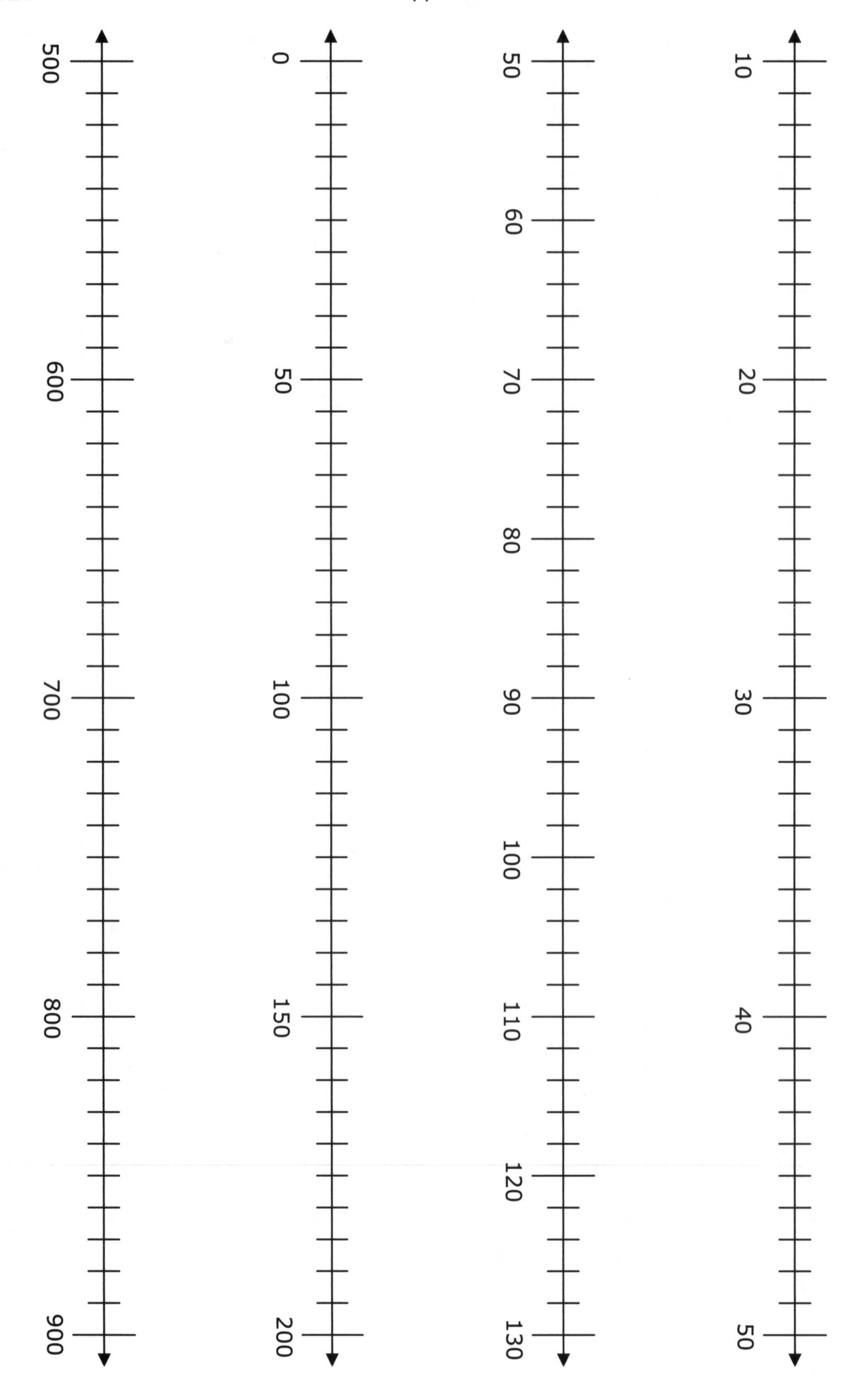
10
20
30
40
50
50
60
70
80
90
100
110
120
130
0
50
100
150
200
500
600
700
800
900

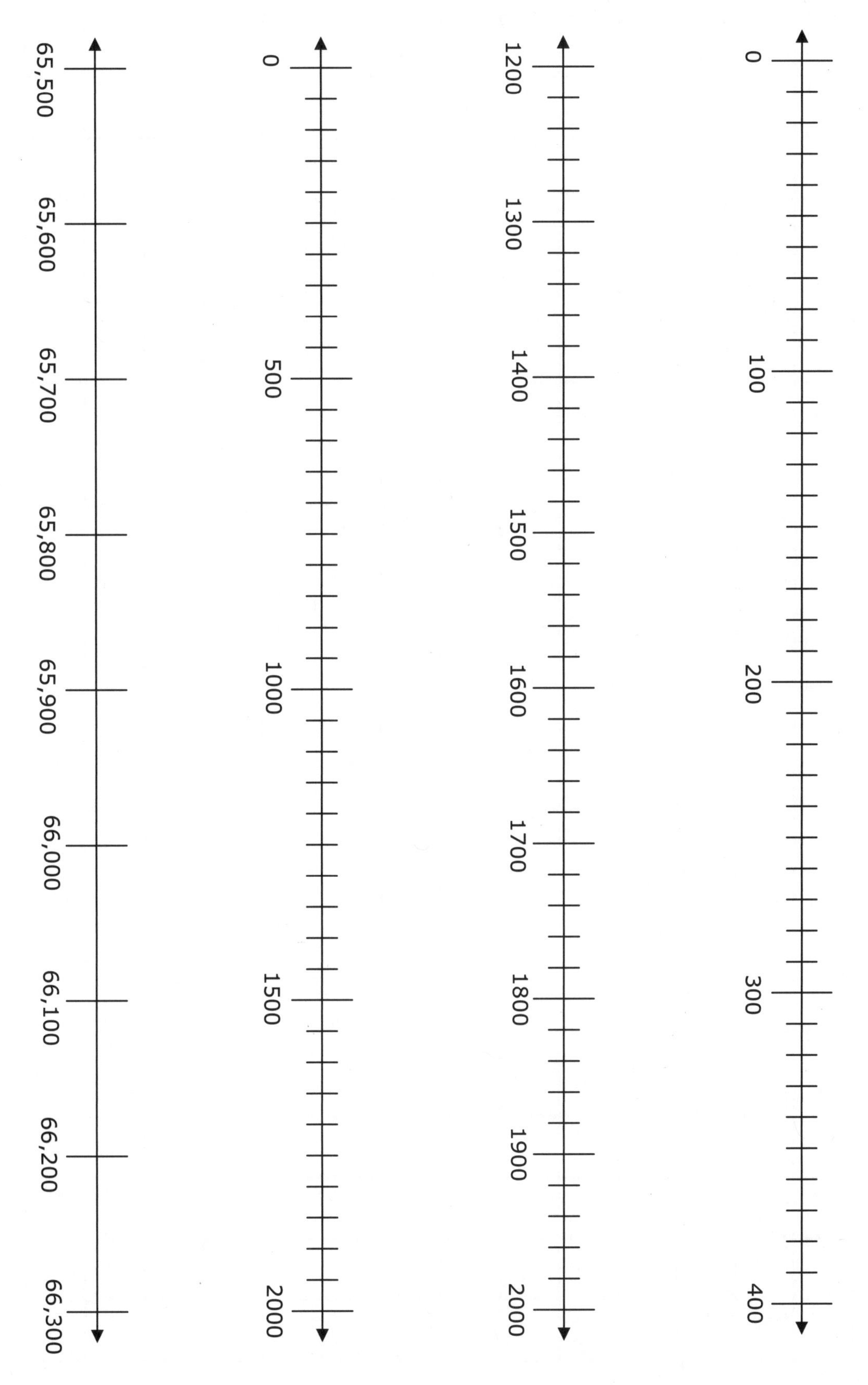
0
100
200
300
400
1200
1300
1400
1500
1600
1700
1800
1900
2000
0
500
1000
1500
2000
65,500
65,600
65,700
65,800
65,900
66,000
66,100
66,200
66,300

4	2	8	5
6	3	☆	12
11	6	7	13
9	2	10	3
4	5	7	☆

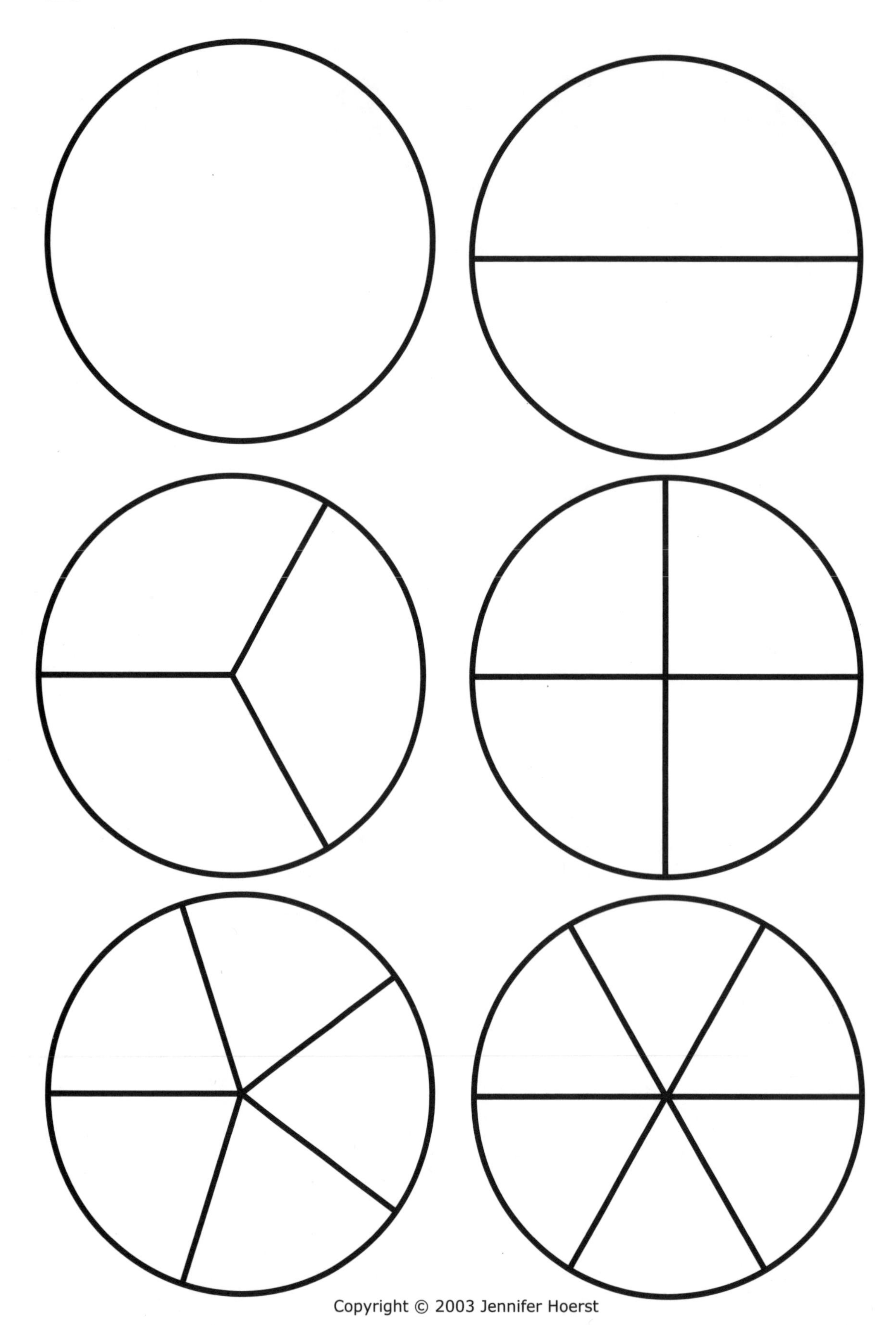

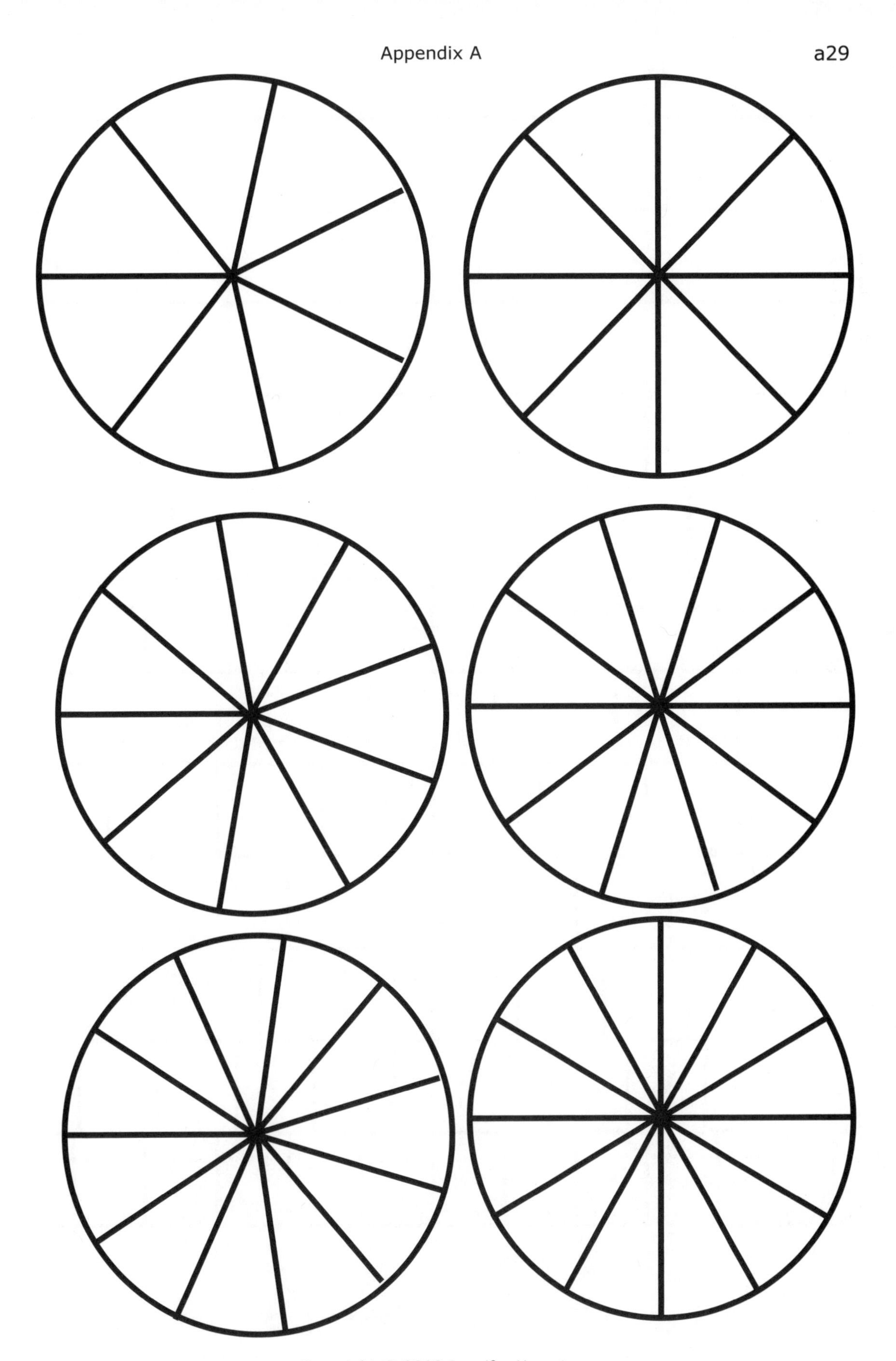

1

$\frac{1}{2}$	$\frac{1}{2}$

$\frac{1}{3}$	$\frac{1}{3}$	$\frac{1}{3}$

$\frac{1}{4}$	$\frac{1}{4}$	$\frac{1}{4}$	$\frac{1}{4}$

$\frac{1}{5}$	$\frac{1}{5}$	$\frac{1}{5}$	$\frac{1}{5}$	$\frac{1}{5}$

$\frac{1}{6}$	$\frac{1}{6}$	$\frac{1}{6}$	$\frac{1}{6}$	$\frac{1}{6}$	$\frac{1}{6}$

$\frac{1}{7}$	$\frac{1}{7}$	$\frac{1}{7}$	$\frac{1}{7}$	$\frac{1}{7}$	$\frac{1}{7}$	$\frac{1}{7}$

$\frac{1}{8}$	$\frac{1}{8}$	$\frac{1}{8}$	$\frac{1}{8}$	$\frac{1}{8}$	$\frac{1}{8}$	$\frac{1}{8}$	$\frac{1}{8}$

$\frac{1}{9}$	$\frac{1}{9}$	$\frac{1}{9}$	$\frac{1}{9}$	$\frac{1}{9}$	$\frac{1}{9}$	$\frac{1}{9}$	$\frac{1}{9}$	$\frac{1}{9}$

$\frac{1}{10}$	$\frac{1}{10}$	$\frac{1}{10}$	$\frac{1}{10}$	$\frac{1}{10}$	$\frac{1}{10}$	$\frac{1}{10}$	$\frac{1}{10}$	$\frac{1}{10}$	$\frac{1}{10}$

$\frac{1}{11}$	$\frac{1}{11}$	$\frac{1}{11}$	$\frac{1}{11}$	$\frac{1}{11}$	$\frac{1}{11}$	$\frac{1}{11}$	$\frac{1}{11}$	$\frac{1}{11}$	$\frac{1}{11}$	$\frac{1}{11}$

$\frac{1}{12}$	$\frac{1}{12}$	$\frac{1}{12}$	$\frac{1}{12}$	$\frac{1}{12}$	$\frac{1}{12}$	$\frac{1}{12}$	$\frac{1}{12}$	$\frac{1}{12}$	$\frac{1}{12}$	$\frac{1}{12}$	$\frac{1}{12}$

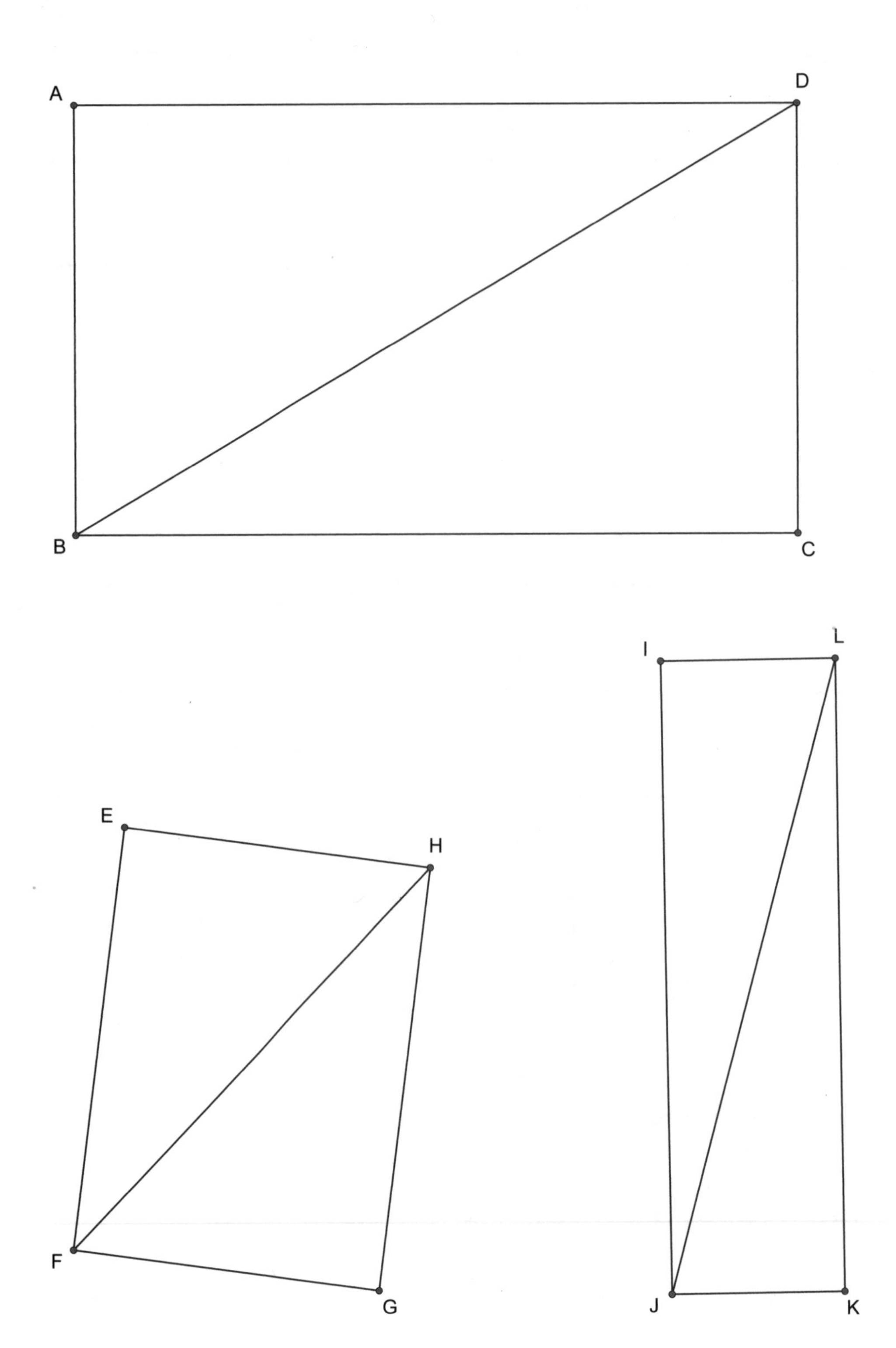
A
D
B
C
I
L
E
H
F
G
J
K